# Wave Therapy

## Your Power To Heal

By

Samuel J. Winters

Winters Publishing, Wichita, Kansas

Wave Therapy is a reflection of the studies, applications and experiences of the author. This book is not meant to suggest to the reader to replace any medical advice or supervision of a medical doctor or other health professional.



ISBN: 0-9661900-0-9

Library of Congress Catalog Card: 97-97124
Winters, Samuel J. 1953 -
Wave Therapy, Your Power To Heal
Includes bibliographical references, glossary, and index

Published by:
Winters Publishing
511 A-E. 2nd St.
Wichita, Kansas 67202

Printed and bound in the United States of America

Editor: Cynthia Snider
Illustrations: Nickie Siegal
Cover Design: Nickie Siegal
Graphics Consultant: Patty Yoon

# ACKNOWLEDGMENTS

There are people in my life that I would like to thank for helping me to become who I am today. All of these people have helped play a role in my adventure of learning what I've discovered to date about healing and wholeness.

Oral Roberts: For your inspiration that God is a good God who desires health and wholeness for all. For your example to me that when working in partnership with God, one could discover that nothing is impossible.

Francis McNutt: For the example of always continuing in the effort of healing with the positive attitude to stick with it, to keep trying and to never give up. For demonstrating that we are all on a continuous journey to understand the partnership between ourselves and God as a never ending process of growth and experience. Thank you for the encouragement that each effort to try is an achievement.

Kathryn Kuhlman: Bless her heart. Even though she is no longer with us, the times I spent in her company were as a mentor of encouragement that God loves and is present with the regular ordinary people of the world that He cares for. She gave her self over fully to the belief that anyone could experience the love of God and she offered her life to declare that insightful wisdom with the world. She always would say, "If one person would just give theirself completely to God, that person could change the world." Her example of living to me was to make yourself available and then watch what God would do.

Rev. Tommy Tyson: A jovial wonderful man who declares that the vastness of the presence of the Creator can be found in the much overlooked wonder of nature. Thanks for teaching how a person touches God when touching nature. How the simplicity of a tree could display the down-home presence of the living God among us.

Abbot George Burke: Thank you for writing your book, Magnetic Therapy, Healing In Your Hands, for the direction it gave in jump starting me in helping others to heal. Not only has the information you passed on changed my life but of the many people over the years that have benefited from my carrying on the example of your work.

Taking up your challenge "to pass it on" has led to my own adaptations of your work and in the contribution of this book.

Norm Shealy, M.D., Ph.D, and Carolyn Myss, Ph.D. : Thank you both for your great contributions to the field of energy medicine. From you I've learned how to better discern, identify and breakdown how to work manually with the individual emotions and attitudes in Wave Therapy to assist in influencing the quality of a person's health and living.

John Diamond, M.D.: For your contributions as well, in your valuable book, Life Energy, that helped confirm for me the value of the attitude of the will to live and its power to effect an individual's overall physical health and well being.

I would also like to thank those persons more close to home these days whose encouragement made this book possible.

MaryJo Grant: Thanks for your faith, encouragement and attitude of doing "Whatever it takes!" For the constant support in "let's see if this works" and courage to experiment in discovering new ways to look at how God works among us. Thanks for your humility and what to me always seemed an over exaggeration of giftedness within me, was still an opinion secretly appreciated.

Randy Winters: Thank you so much for your brotherly support of encouraging me to keep at it through all the tough times of writing. Your words of, "You can do it!" kept me going to where this book finally became a reality.

Mary A: A powerful director at my grocery store checkout stand who unknown to her kept me focused on who I was writing to; us regular folks. Thank you for your wonderful enthusiasm.

Nickie Siegal: Thanks for your enduring patience and talent in turning my vague explanations of hand positions and stick man figures in to a contribution of visual art. It was a learning adventure for both of us. Thanks for your spirit of joy, and for listening to my stories.

Patty Yoon: Patty, Patty, Patty. Thanks so much for your straightforwardness in offering your insightful opinions on graphic design and layout to help make this writing more visually appealing.

Cynthia Snider: My wonderful editor. Gee. I had no idea the complexity punctuation could be in making something readable! Thank you for your much needed help and encouragement to keep it simple.

All the people I've worked with: My thanks to all the men and women whose names I can barely begin to mention who have let me practice on them to see what would happen. You all were the ones who helped me in this ongoing journey of adventure and discovery that has made this book possible. I have to mention some of you: Margaret, Arlys Marie, Cindy, Linda, Sue, Jeff, Dwight, Virginia, Mary, Rose Ann, Devon and Connie, Calder, Laurie, Mary Jo, Martha, Howie, Lois, Celeste, Lyn, Ben, Laura, Doug, Patricia, Don and Merleyn, Charlotte, Dorothy, Edie, Greg, Julie, Karen, Kathy, Sue, Dave, Brenda, Sandy, Michelle, Nathan, Joanie, Dennis, Armanda,...and...and...hugs to everyone of you! I'm sure I have left many people out. My thanks also to you.

Mom and Dad: For everything that you are in your constant reflection of God in the attitudes of joy and optimism in every situation no matter how difficult the obstacles may be. Because of you I am who I am today.

The Angels: To the countless new acquaintances of angels who just by your presence showed me that whatever judgments and objections I can come up with about my inadequacies that they're just not relevant in the face of God. If angels ever read books, thanks for showing me how participation with the will of God is to work at my becoming more whole.

God: Thank you for sharing a glimpse of yourself concerning the great mystery of your grace from which you freely offer to all, the power of life.

# PREFACE

I had a goal. I needed to find out if it was true or not that the power of God was with mankind on earth to heal.

I, like many, wanted to have an answer. The information here is a sample of what I've discovered to date in helping with offering an answer to this question. What you will find here is certainly not a claim to have found the complete answer by any means so no need to expect this writing to have all the answers. This world is made up of far richer mysteries than any imagination or experience can come up with than can be dealt with in these chapters.

I have though come to one simple understanding; within all nature there is a built-in system of recovery. The human body has a remarkable system to heal itself. That is evident to anyone who is able to get over the common cold. Healing may not come so easily for some and certainly not without a lot of discomfort, but for the most part we all eventually do.

I've also come to the conclusion that being created as we are to naturally overcome disease and sickness that by design it must be what God wants for us. The failure to overcome disease in that light therefore does not mean God doesn't desire health and healing for us, or has a certain macabre enjoyment in seeing us suffer, it's just that we don't always know how to do it. The failure to overcome disease is our lack of knowing the principles to apply towards maintaining better health.

Science, medicine and religion in history have all shared the same desire to answer the riddle of disease and how to overcome it. Often from different and opposing perspectives but still have the same objectives in mind; to understand, and to get results from the application of the understanding. So, in this book I present nothing new really that hasn't been understood and practiced since the beginning of recorded history. It's an offering of my studies and practice of a time honored and tested manner towards healing that I have found has worked time and time again for people. It's a simple and easy process I believe anyone can participate in that helps meet a common goal for all of us when it comes to sickness; to get better.

The first section, Part One, will go over information of some simple laws of biology and physics that you already know. This section is a primer to understanding how and why Wave Therapy works according the natural laws of creation. If you want to skip it all and go directly to Part Two, the "How To Do It" section, feel free to go right ahead. You don't have to know the information in the first section to begin working Wave Therapy effectively. You can follow the examples for working with common health problems and still get results regardless of understanding why the hand positions work. I learned all the information presented here by experimenting and so can you. I recommend you do read it though, especially the physics information to help make more informed decisions about how to make use of the different influences of energy flowing through your hands.

You'll find I've presented the information like a review of a childhood science class and is treated as such with some fun clipart. It's my way of approaching what to some readers would be the more tedious and mechanical part of the material with a touch of lightness and humor to help you get through it.

Part Two, the "How To Do It," section, offers the how's and why's of working Wave Therapy for common everyday health complications. The whole Body Work-Up section is for those interested in working with more chronic health problems. Enjoy the art!

Part Three, takes it all a step further in working with long distance healing. This subject will deal more with the sense of spirituality behind Wave Therapy that offers a perspective of prayer by way of the physics of spiritual communication.

Once more thing. These pages are dotted with references to God that overall gives silent praise to a shared view with the psalmist, David, how we and all of creation are "fearfully and wonderfully made."[1] Although I'm Christian in religious orientation, my experience and opinion is that religious outlook makes no difference in the working of Wave Therapy. For any complications the reader may have towards these references due to the title name I use of God, know, for myself, it's out of simplicity. To offer a perspective of what I mean by this name here's one of my favorite explanations: "God is mystery. God is "the wholly Other," invisible, inconceivable,

[1] Psalms 139:14, KJV

radically transcendent, beyond all words, beyond all understanding."[2] Should you have a different name for the divine which you feel more comfortable with to apply to this reference, scratch out the one I use and put your own in.

I trade off the use of the term energy with my favorite phrase, the power of life. The revelation and sharing of the life of God in the form today we term as energy has been given many names and meanings throughout time. The Chinese called it Chi, The Japanese; Ki, the Egyptians; Ka (body of light), the Eastern Indians; Prana. In more recent history names such as the Odic force (or Odyllic force), Anton Mesmer's (from whom hypnotism emerged from) Animal Magnetism, vital force, orgone energy, bio-energy, electromagnetic energy, vital fluid and others. In Christian tradition this power could be referred to as "The breath of life", the power of God, or the power of the Holy Spirit. The affects of coming in contact with this power has led me to tack a term to it for myself. So, I have. It's called in my terms simply the ***Power of Life.***

I invite you to take a look at what's here within these pages, practice and judge for yourself the many benefits Wave Therapy can bring into your life. Presented are my own views of biology, physics and spirituality. How these areas offer simple insights on the laws of health and healing that can be found in recognizing the will of God in nature. A spiritual science if you will, that encompasses a range of thought with a conclusion that there is power available freely all around us and within everyone who is willing to take action to participate. To participate in receiving the healing benefits of the Power of Life!

---

[2] The Orthodox Way, Bishop Kallistos Ware

# Table Of Contents

# FOREWARD

Once in awhile, a person comes into ones life who is gifted in ways that enrich, inspire, teach and heal. Sam Winters is such a person in my life. We have worked together for four years and I consider him a good friend, patient mentor and gifted healer.

I have received regular Wave Therapy treatments from him that have eliminated the symptoms of a type of arthritis that has no known cure; in addition, I have healed from all sorts of lesser diseases. I tell him that his work keeps my body, soul, and spirit in a "healing mode."

I have also observed how others have responded to energy work or "physical prayer" as he calls it. There have been true miracles when we have known that we have been graced by God.

Sam is extremely intuitive, highly spiritually attuned and intellectually honest. These characteristics have enabled him to be a conduit through which God works to teach the connection between body, soul, spirit and the wholeness that is God's will for us.

Sam insists that this is a very practical book for we both have found that healing is practical and natural. You are about to unlearn some 'facts' about healing and health and God and prayer and wholeness. I assure you that knowing Sam through this book will change you as you open your heart, mind and spirit to consider his ideas and concepts.

May God bless you as you begin this healing journey.

Mary Jo Grant, B.S., M.S., Ph.D. Candidate
Counselor

# AUTHOR'S NOTE

Do you want to appear stupid and feel embarrassed?

Some question, huh? Who wants to do that?! But you probably will when you first try the methods outlined here to facilitate natural healing that I present to you in this book. You'll get over it though once you try it. I say that because you're bound to feel a bit hesitant to try them. I certainly did. Why? Because this approach to healing is so embarrassingly simple you're sure to think to yourself "This is too crazy to work!" Especially, for example, when you offer to help someone who is suffering from the pain of arthritis. You might say, "Nothing could really happen to help someone get better by simply holding my hands over a painful area." But I can tell you from personal experience that if you try it at least ONCE you'll see for yourself that the power to assist others to heal is as close to you as your own hands.

You'll also discover that this ability to heal is natural to everyone. It's a built in ability that everyone has. Which means even you can do it! To find out if it's really true you do have to try it first and that will take a little action on your part. That's the first step in getting results. You have to do it. Reading about it may be interesting but until you act, the experience won't be yours.

To help you get over the intimidation that sickness and disease may have in holding back your efforts in attempting to try Wave Therapy it would be helpful to know a little of the how's and why's of disease and sickness and how this approach to "therapy" works to help promote wholeness. So before offering you these simple tools to facilitate your practice of assisting others to heal, I'll explain what I have discovered to date of the laws of health. Some of the information may well be challenging to your beliefs about how I see the physical and spiritual worlds in operation. Good! You could probably use a little stirring up. You'll be all the better for it before it's over. So will the person or people in your family or circle of friends whom you'll practice with.

It's going to be a presentation of simple things of which you already understand. There may even be a few perspectives you may have not considered before.

## MY GUARANTEE

I can guarantee you this one thing. The information you'll find in these pages will alter your outlook on your ability to manage your health for the rest of your born days.

So get ready.

Get comfortable.

Here we go!

# My Story

## How It All Began

# My Story

## *How It All Began*

"Try it out! See if you can heal my knee," said Mary Jo.

Mary Jo seemed confident this discovery of mine would work. That if I held my hands beside her knee some kind of power would work to heal her. She certainly had more faith than I did. Of course, for her there was nothing to lose really in this experiment. Her knee was so damaged that she was considering surgery to have an artificial knee to replace her own worn out one. So, a chance of anything to make her knee work better was an option worth considering.

Mary Jo was one who always considered the available options. For me there was a hesitation to act so quickly to her request. As eager as I was to try out this approach to healing, some unresolved issues were holding me back. This challenge for healing was a confrontation of beliefs that were almost ready to give way for a new understanding but old thoughts were still lingering on causing me to hesitate a moment. You see, I had adopted a point of view that said all healing comes from God, which specifically meant to me only Christians held the rights to that power. A pretty predjudiced point of view. If this thing worked, then is would be true that anyone could work healing regardless of their beliefs. For this method was not dependent on someone's religious belief. It worked solely on an ability all persons by nature held in their hands. Anybody could do it. Here was a challenge before me that was leading me into a new understanding of reality.

### The Test

"Try it out, and heal my knee." she had said.

OOPS! I was caught. I had stumbled across a book about this unusual art of healing and was curious to try it out and see if it would work. It's one thing to read about it. Quite another to see if it's true.

We were in the "Group Room" affectionately named where Mary Jo holds her growth group meetings. She was sitting across from me, both of us facing each other. Her in the easy chair, knee waiting, with me sitting on the sofa. Deciding to take up her challenge I scooted forward and placed my hands in position. The left one on one side, the right hand on the other. Not touching. About three inches away from her leg.

And we waited.

We waited for about ten seconds. Then it happened.

Movement began. The knee cap started moving. All on its own! So were my eyes. They were wide open in amazement. I looked up quickly to see how Mary Jo was responding. Her eyes were in the same condition as mine, wide open in wonder.

Together we both looked backed down in time to watch the knee cap continue to move over about an inch to my right. Then slowly. . . it moved back. We both looked up at each other again. I'm sure I must have looked as astonished as she did. I would have moved my hands away then if it weren't for the amazement making me forget I was holding my hands where they were.

"Oh, my God," was all I could manage to say.

There were more surprises yet to come.

## Looking For Direction

Let me back up from here and start at the beginning. I got myself in this awkward position because I had been visiting Mary Jo to discuss my dreams. She's a professional counselor with one of her jobs being in working with people to help them understand where their dreams may be giving them direction in their lives; believing that God can speak to us through the language of dreams. I certainly needed that kind of chat. For I was stumped. My life was going no where, at least as far as I could tell. In looking down the road ahead it seemed the prospects of my future enjoyment of life was destined to be as thrilling as the last ten years, if I didn't get a handle on something to get me out the rut I was in. Every day seemed the same thing. Nothing new. Everything else I had tried in philosophy, prayer and direction didn't do the trick so here I was talking over the dreams I was having for the last three weeks to see what I could learn from them about myself. Maybe there was a chance something in them would reveal what I was missing. My hope was that God had set up dreaming as one way of getting helpful messages across. I certainly couldn't detect any messages around me from anywhere else as much as I tried to notice. The only noticeable change that seemed to have some promise for me was I had gotten to the place where I chose to believe if all else fails, try faith. Faith that God would do what in the scriptures He said He would do, "In all your ways acknowledge Him, And He will direct your path." [1]

Well, I believed I could vouch for my end of the deal. I could acknowledge Him pretty good, I thought. I figured a lifetime of it. Making sure I believed "truth," kept my nose clean, dedicating myself to religious fervor and above all don't do anything God wouldn't do!

But frankly, my attitude had come down to "So what good has it done me?"

Then the thought had occurred to me, "What if God HAS been directing me and I just haven't noticed? Maybe I hadn't paid attention or even worse ignored the direction because it got in the way of what I believed? Meaning, what I believed about God, and how He worked. I had all my concepts of God canned and stored on the shelf labeled, "This is how God does things." With directions on the label, "Open, pour contents in to a 9" saucepan, heat for ten minutes at medium, and eat as is." That simple. To admit there might be someone else who had a different can of goods, whose concept recommended "adding water, and salt to taste" would be a difficult set of directions to follow. But, hey! If that's what it was going to take? I was willing at this point.

So, I figured I'll try to be watchful. Put off any resistance for change and expect that the day is full of direction. I would be bold and even consider different directions. I just had to expect that He was really doing His end or the scripture that ". . .He will direct your path" would be just a lie, wouldn't it? So, one of us was not looking at this verse right. Figuring, God doesn't make mistakes like that, the problem had to be with me. I knew I had been stubborn about the way He ought to direct. So, I decided to try a new approach and watch for anything, do anything, go anywhere and listen, follow, and see where it leads me. Hopefully it would lead to somewhere interesting.

---

1 Proverbs 3:6

## Finding Direction in Unlikely Places

Funny how it works out; leading that is. It seems God doesn't seem to be all that concerned about informing me outright about what He's doing. I'd like to think God needs my input and approval for His actions. Instead it's more like He waits just up ahead for me to make a move. As though He likes the surprise that comes with discovery. I guess it's His way. I tend to stay back.

Personally, I don't really like it that way. I would much rather have some simple and clear cut writing on the wall. Even a letter in the mail would do. Or, how about getting direction in life like one of those treasure hunt games that gives you clues to the next spot? And if you can't figure out the clue there's a handy phone number to call and someone on the other end tells you straight out where to go next. That's my fantasy ideal of good directioning. But nope, that's not the way it is for me. I'm not told how to live and what to do like that. What I get is more like "You say you believe and have faith that I direct? Then act like it. Put your feet where your faith is and start walking. You'll find me just up a head." So, I determined that since nothing shows up in my mail box to help, and the walls were still clean of miraculous writings, or waiting for directions to be boomed out over a heavenly intercom system didn't work, and since I wasn't good at unraveling possible clues I figured, now what? How about just following where your feet take you and look into everything as if God is everywhere? And knows what He's doing?

Novel idea!

So a few days later I found myself walking into a bookstore. The kind I would *never* go in. Why? Because I believed the particular books found there lead people away from "the truth." They had occult stuff on astrology, psychic readers, channeling, crystals and incense everywhere. All the taboo things devout Christians are required to avoid. Things "of the devil." Nevertheless, here I was. I was there because I was working on adopting a new point of view. One which said "perhaps I didn't know everything." Everything that it is, about truth. Quite an appalling concept. I didn't realize how arrogant I was about this. I believed Christians had *thee* truth about everything. As soon as everybody else caught up with that fact the world would just be great. Well, I had as much 'truth' as the next fundamentalist and life was not that great. That's what got me thinking I needed to understand more because what I did know wasn't working. That fact,

I was facing up to. I was finding the arrogance of my religious exclusion was slipping out from under me. And I had to find a firmer place to stand on.

One area I wanted firming up in was I needed authenticity. I wanted God to be more real in the physical life than just spiritual. Instead of stillness in prayer, I wanted action in the down home real world where I lived!

So here I was about to act on an impulse to go inside this store that I'd seen at a glance while driving down a street. I did have a sense of fearful excitement. After all, it was a day of quest, watching and acting on expectation that direction was actually being given. I had figured I'd try getting out and drive around and just see what may happen even among the smallest things that occur to give me clues. Clues like running into someone that may say something important that I would normally miss by not paying attention. So today I was going to pay attention to anything that happens, follow the lead and see where it takes me. I was on a test mission. And here was my first test, an impulse to go into this store.

At first I resisted because I felt I may be wrong in assuming God may lead in this way by following impulses. If this didn't work out this kind of leading was based on nothing more than the moments urging. But that's all I knew how to work with on this plan; going with an intuition. But I had resolved to follow after any chance of leading to become a hopeful confirmation to foster my new attitude.

The store was a new business as part of building project for the downtown development. I was driving east when I spotted the store's hanging sign dangling from under the roof of the entrance. That's when I got the impulse. The feeling came as a challenge. I decided to go for it and see what happens. I drove around the block to find my way back around through the maze of one-way streets and alley ways. I found the sign again and parked in front of the door. I looked up through my truck windshield and read the small sign.

"A New Age Bookstore"

This was a New Age Store! This wasn't right. I didn't go into New Age stores. Some leading. This is all wrong. I'm not getting the hang of this at all. God must not intend to lead by following impulses for He wouldn't lead me here. Then the thought occurred to me if I turn away from going down any new road I don't like I'm assuming that God isn't there. But He's supposed to be everywhere. So, somehow He must be there too. Even in a New Age bookstore however opposing that idea. I get out of my truck and walk up the few iron stair steps that led to the front door and go in. A little door bell over head tinkling my arrival.

So, here I was standing around in a New Age book store semi-composed as if I was a visitor in a foreign country trying to not look like a tourist. Feeling like a tourist I figured If I learned the language at least that way I would fit in better and be more accepted. You know, be one of the locals. After a greeting of "hello" to the desk attendant sitting behind the counter to my right I began my stroll around the store to learn what I could pick up. I felt awkward.

No, awkward is not the word. Slightly paranoid is better. I was worried actually. Worried about what may rub off on me while in there? I was seeing all these things clearly set forth in the old testament scriptures as forbidden. I saw books on astrology, magic, fortune telling, crystal balls, Buddha's and a corner for people to give "readings" of your past and future. What was I doing here? With that bit of self evaluation I decided it was time to make a smooth exit. This was all wrong for me and could lead me no where. I turned and slowly made my way from the back of the little shop where I had found myself in order to get back up to the front desk and sneak safely out the front door.

The plan was simple. Once back up front I would hang around a second as though "just looking" and slide casually out the door. Reaching my first destination I stood there at the counter with my eyes wondering over all the weird stuff in the glass casing. Looking, but not looking. Waiting for a few seconds to go by for the planned exit to seem appropriate. I would as an extra move scan the book shelf to the left as the final act in this scene as in looking for something and finding it not there, then leave. Just like any other normal person on a shopping cruise. I was just about done with the charade when my eyes after roaming over the bottom of the shelf spotted a little book nestled off in the right hand corner. The cover had two hands with what seemed to be rays of something coming off of the tips of the fingers. Hmmm? My attention caught. Something familiar. I sauntered over and picked it up. My exit plan interrupted.

The title was "Magnetic Therapy, Healing In Your Hands."

What in the world was this? Who wrote it? Abbot George Burke. Abbott? A Christian[2] book in a New Age Bookstore? Who would of thought? But, here it was. Gotta look inside. If a Christian wrote it, it couldn't be all that bad.

I opened the book to hurriedly flip through it a bit. I was hurrying because that certain paranoia feeling was still with me. Not that there was something wrong with the book but somebody might see me. That Christian somebody walking by the store window will see I'm in here. Me, a Christian, not only in a New Age store but actually reading one of those books! The longer I stayed the higher the chances I would be seen through the window behind the counter. That's paranoia for you. Thinking anyone could walk by and catch me in the act of being in such a store. Surely they would say, "Look, there's Sam. What's he doing in there?" I daydreamed up that they'd also think "He's stepped over and gone to the other side. He's snared. The devil has got his hooks in him."

I was ready to dart under the pressure of my imagination, but my feet were stuck to the floor.

I wondered that hopefully something in this book would redeem its presence here in such a store. To validate my reasons for being in there. That would give me reason to linger a little while longer to check the book out. I considered too, that these New Age people sure are accommodating to include everybody as they do like this Christian book. The author's Abbot status seemed awfully redeemable for my excursion in to no-man's land.

I quickly flipped through the pages to see if there was something I could handle. I wanted to be careful. It may be written by a Christian but he also may be weird. Then I ran across the thing that clinched the deal inwardly to give in to buy something in my first visit to a New Age book Store. A tip on "tingling in your hands."

## A Sense Of Power

This is a slightly embarrassing thing. One of the private weird things about myself I normally don't tell just anyone about. It's about a peculiar habit of mine I've picked up over the years concerning a sensation of tingling power I get at times.

---

[2] A Gnostic faith

For years I've been getting this odd feeling that comes over my body. This tingling sensation. It feels like a radiating sense of some kind of power. It usually moves over my hands and at times ends up moving up my arms and sometimes surrounding my whole body. At those moments I'm simply filled with awe. It's nothing I do. It just happens. When these sensations happen even my waking awareness is affected. An awareness of the awesome power of life around me. The presence of greatness. I had noticed this feeling also comes over me during prayer and always during praying for someone during intercession, praying on their behalf. But, I had no real clues about what it meant practically. I could only figure that it was probably something from God, but what? That was one of the things I was wanting direction in. For the sensations had always been a puzzle.

Sometimes while I'm just walking around it happens. Over the years I've learned to expect the sensation to come over my hands when in public. Especially in any crowd mingling. Mall trips are a sure thing. But still no reason behind it ever made itself clear to me.

The reference in the book was the first time I had ever seen anything close to addressing the issue. As I read a little farther the author was speaking of how to calm down the effects of tingling over the body by grounding yourself to the earth! These words reminded me of a similar experience I had where trees do the same for me.

One time years ago while observing the beauty of a clear night summer sky above the familiar tingling sensation began building in my hands. The beauty of nature around me was affecting a deepening appreciation for the handiwork of creation. The more I contemplated the wonder of it all the more my body was being enveloped in a tingling sense as though somehow this was a response to wonder. The feeling had not only moved through my hands but up my arms and covered my shoulders and back. My feet had started too feel it also. Slowly the sensations had moved up from there to my legs and ended up covering my whole body. It was quite a wonderful peaceful experience that struck me as well with humility of my place in the grandeur of the universe around me. The only other times I experienced this whole body sensation was in a few healing prayer meetings. If it got intense enough I found I could hardly move or speak. Sometimes when it happened I couldn't speak for days. I couldn't because it seemed the very act of speaking would profane the ongoing sense of the presence of something holy.

That particular night I had been walking down a sidewalk to my apartment when the tingling sensations began. I had just looked up to view the stars and the familiar sensation started. I was about twenty feet from the front door of my apartment when what I can only then describe as the power of life and holy wonder was causing me to loose mobility being so caught up in it. I could only stop and wait for the ebb to occur. When these moments come they would slowly pass with time. I'd just have to wait till it passed.

But this time I wanted to get inside my apartment. Being seen at that late hour standing suspiciously by myself on a sidewalk in the middle of the night may give cause for concern. How would I explain my behavior? If I could even talk! Something had to be done.

I spotted a little tree next to the side walk I was on and I managed to shuffle slowly over to it. Other times I had learned that sticking my feet in some dirt would do the trick. Something about doing that calmed me down. But for the immediate purpose it came to mind the tree would do as well. A tree had roots and they were in the ground. It seemed a reasonable alternative route for the moment than taking my shoes off and finding some hole in the earth for dirt to stick my feet in. By then I could hardly move any way. So, what I had in mind seemed OK and the thing to do at the moment.

When I managed to reach the tree I just grabbed on to the poor thing and held on with both hands. The hold on the tree did the trick. It was like a ground wire that immediately began drawing off the energy I felt around me. Within a few minutes I was pretty much back to normal and could walk again. I made it the next few feet to my apartment door and I was in.

Since that time I have hugged a fair amount of trees in my day!

The talk in this book I was looking at was about putting your feet in the earth to balance your "magnetism." I had no idea about this magnetism stuff but I knew about the occasional need to go stick my feet in the dirt sometimes or the next best thing to grab on to a tree. This guy knew something. So my attention was caught. This Abbot guy seemed to know more about these body sensations then anyone else I'd run across. The next few flips of a page had me reading about the tingling sensations as part of helping people to heal. That was it! I was sold! Surely he had more to say that I needed to learn. So, I found something after all in a New Age Bookstore that was going to be helpful. I had been praying for years for some kind of understanding what this tingling thing was about and what it meant. I had been earnestly looking for reality in the Christian walk. A walk that proved God was involved with life. That God wanted people healed. I wanted to do that, and to prove it was possible. Such proof would authenticate my beliefs of a caring God. Maybe this power sensation had something to do with an answer to my prayers?

Somewhere there may have been other clues about these hands of mine and I had missed it down the road. This little book appeared to offer the first answer to my question. It was a strange circumstance where this attempting at following intuition had taken me. Not my first choice by any means. But I was beginning to understand, who was I to judge that? If the answer comes, it comes. The where and who it comes through is none of my concern to judge as right or wrong. Just that I get the message. That's what's important.

I remember a story in the Bible where an angel spoke to a man through an ass. I'd rather not refer myself to the animal as a description of my own attitude . . .so, I decided to swallow my pride and bought my first book to become of New Age shopper.

I read it cover to cover three times by the next day. It was exciting to think that what this man had to say might by true. The sensations I hand in my hands all these years was a natural force of power God had placed in nature. He called it "Magnetism," and everybody has it. You have to have it or you simply aren't alive. If you are depleted in this force you get sick. If it flourishes well, you have the strength to stay well. That's the basics. And he gave some techniques for hand placements that affect the flow of energy to increase the body's natural ability to heal itself.

So, here I was the next day about to end another session with Mary Jo when I decided to tell her about the book. I told her how simple the technique for healing therapy was and wouldn't it be amazing if something so simple actually worked.

What if it didn't work? Then where would I be? I'd be left with no direction again. And a crazy mixed up wrong idea again about how God leads.

Then again what if it did work? Then where would I be? Certainly not where I was. And isn't that what I'd been wanting, to not be where I was but some place new? If this worked in any way, my life would change. This was the test to see if I was willing for change. If all this time the directions were there, then God in His greatness has been there all the time and I just was not aware of it. He was there as close as my hands and I didn't know it. How ironic that would be. If nothing did happen, I'd still be where I was, with another door closed. This door however was here before me to try and open. Nothing to do but to face it, turn the handle, open it, walk through and see what was on the other side.

And that's when the challenge came. . .the test.

I had opened the door, walked through and something was happening. Mary Jo's knee was responding, moving on it's own under some kind of power.

## The Rest Of The Story

Mary Jo just stared at me. Eyes still open wide. Then she suddenly looked down. My eyes followed. Her knee was moving again. Our eyes both riveted to the scene.

This time it moved even farther, with the whole of the knee slowly bending inward to the right. It was incredible. Just as though some invisible finger was gently pushing the whole leg and knee over.

Now I was getting excited.

"This really works!" I thought.

Seems Mary Jo had ended up being surprised herself. But more was still to come.

I dutifully held my hands in place determined to see this thing through all though not knowing how long that would be. What was already happening was far more than I had expected. Actually, I had no idea what to expect. Certainly not this. Or even what was to happen next.

The knee moved back.

We stared in silence. And waited for what may come next, if anything. We weren't disappointed. Three to five seconds later the whole leg started to bend inward. So much so I had to follow it with my hands just to keep them in place. I held them a little wider to accommodate the motion. The leg seemed to have a will and mind of it's own.

When the leg had moved in about twelve inches Mary Jo suddenly clasped both hands to the arm of the chair and sat up bolt straight in her chair. Eyes bugged.

What was going on now!? I was getting a little apprehensive here. I found I couldn't say a thing. This was beyond any thing I had expected. Actually, I hadn't expected much of anything to happen. Yet here we both were in the middle of something quite profound.

"Something is moving up my leg" she whispered startled and staring at me in surprise.

All I could do was sit in helpless silence. Not knowing how to respond.

"It feels like some kind of energy is moving up the outside of my leg!" she said louder.

I quickly turned my attention back to her leg and as I did I heard Mary Jo's voice climb as she hung on to the arms of the chair.

"Ohhhhhhhhhh!" and then a sound. . . POP!

Her right hip pops with a loud cracking noise. Like the kind you would hear during an adjustment in a chiropractor's office.

"My right hip just popped!" she says in what was now becoming more a mood of calm astonishment as she was quieting down. She was settling back down in to her chair and seemed to be thrilled over the experience.

Slowly the knee moves back to its original position and I assume it's all over. At least *I'm* done. This was an extraordinary adventure for one day. And I lifted away my hands.

To say the least, amazement is a little word to describe the moment. And I sit back and slump into the sofa.

"What just happened" I asked trying to make sense of the experience. Hopefully she could offer a good explanation of the event. After all it was her knee.

She explained the sensation of the knee as simply moving over on it's own and a feeling what was like an energy moving slowly up her leg from the knee. Then the energy flow picked up speed toward the end, shot up to her hip and then the big pop! She felt wonderful and exhilarated. And suddenly full of ideas.

"Do you have any idea what this means?" she asked.

I was still too shocked myself to think of anything. But not Mary Jo. That trained psychologist's mind of hers was going a mile a minute, evaluating the possibilities.

Not only did she have a problem knee but was also suffering from Fibromyalgia[3], a muscle disease that causes debilitating pain. She was wondering if this could help with that condition.

I had no clue. But whatever was happening, it was powerful. And since we had gone this far, why not try it out on her whole body not just the knee? We could try a full body treatment and see what happens. So we scheduled to try it out the next week when she had some free time. I would study up and get prepared for the event.

The results we witnessed that day and the days to follow were to be lessons in healing beyond both our expectations. We were entering a different world found behind a newly opened door. A world full of surprises to come with new understandings.

Since that first meeting I've had the privilege of working with people bearing the burden of all kinds of diseases and ailments from the common cold to cancer. Each with some kind of improvement in his or her condition whether it be from emotional relief, physical tension released or outright recovery.

The rest of this book is about some of what I've witnessed and learned since the first experience with Mary Jo.[4] Some of it you may not find compatible with your beliefs. That's all right with me. I would hope whatever you may find uncomfortable will not prevent you from at least looking into the ideas and the experiences presented here. They're just my experiences. That's what I was and still am looking for, experiences of healing that work in the real world. My world. If that's what you're looking for too, take what works for you. Change them if you should discover a way in your own experience that works better. That's the one thing we all can count on. Change. My life was not changing; it was stagnant. I'm seeing now through Wave Therapy that the world is so full of mystery; it's a playground of discovery that can keep me in continuous wonder for the rest of my life. Making new discoveries is what makes living fun for me and a life worth living. This healing work is one of those mysteries.

Healing is an exciting process of becoming whole, discovering the many ways God displays and offers His life, upon which anyone can

---

[3] Fibromyalgia (Fibro-my-al-ja), A muscular disease with pain in between the layers of tissue separating the skin and muscles. There is no known cause or cure.

[4] Mary Jo today exercises by walking a mile a day without pain in her knee. She also claims she no longer has Fibromyalgia.

draw upon freely to live abundantly. That's what led me onward to my next step. To find out if this particular healing ability is available to everyone or just a few special people? If it is for everyone, where is the evidence?

## Onward

The next stop along my route for getting answers about God's healing power was to study the world around me. The Bible has written that the attributes of God are displayed in creation. "For the invisible things of him since the creation of the world are clearly seen, being perceived through the things that are made, *even* his everlasting power and divinity; that they may be without excuse." [5]

I wanted to find out how true that was and what the verse meant. So next is what I came up with; the Power of Life found in creation.

[5] Romans 1:20

# Part I

# Biology and Physics

## The Wonder Of Nature

# Biology And Health

## *The Science Of Life*

### What Makes A Clock Tick?

Such a profound question! See I told you we'd start simple.

A clock ticks because you wind it up. That was in the old days. Today, clocks operate on batteries, or we simply plug them in a wall socket. With some clocks there are even solar panels. No telling what they may come up with next. However a clock ticks it's because there is a power source that runs it. That's an obvious conclusion, isn't it?

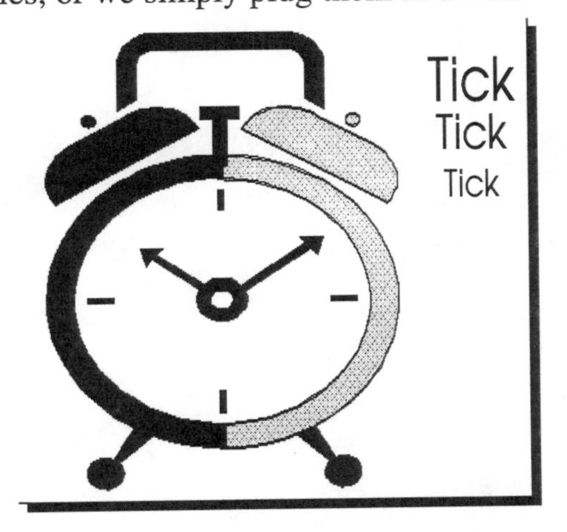


Equally obvious is how the human body functions. Just like that ticking clock, we tick because there's a power that runs us, which we normally think of as being the heart. Everybody knows that. However, without a power source to run your heart you will fall over on your face, never to rise again. We need power to run everything in our bodies. The heart, the brain, the lungs, all the organs, the muscles and the nervous system all need power to run. This power is experienced as ***energy.***

### Where Does Energy Come From?

Everyone can come up with at least one answer for this one. The first one most likely to come to mind is that we get our source of energy from the ***food*** we eat. What a wonderful thing eating can be. For me eating is a true pleasure moment. Maybe that's why this one source of energy comes to mind so easily. There are three other main sources from which we also get energy, but we don't usually give them much of our attention or credit. We also get energy from the ***air*** we breathe. The lungs take in air so we can get energy from oxygen. Don't forget ***water!*** Without it we simply don't live very long. We also get energy from ***sunlight***. Light is a source of energy we don't normally think of, but it's where we get our vitamin D from that helps regulates the flow of calcium for the health of bones.

We can come up with four common items we casually depend on to survive.

1. ***Food***
2. ***air***
3. ***water*** and
4. ***sunlight***

I believe we can all agree that we need all four of these to stay alive and well. Within our bodies is the wonderful ability to find and get the energy out of these elements that empowers us to live.

To assist you in thinking about our reliance on these four sources of energy a little more, I'll add some quick thoughts about just how much we rely on them.

Let's start with. . .

## FOOD. . .My favorite

No one in recorded history has survived longer than forty days without it, and that historical figure is pretty well known.[3]

If we were to apply a rating scale to our energy sources, food earns a rating of. . .

**# 4.**

## Now for WATER. . .

[3] You win if you said Jesus. There have been recorded cases of those called Breatharians who claim to exist solely on the energy they are able to draw in from the air around them. Strange, but true. I don't recommend the practice, however. Personally, I prefer eating.

No one has ever sustained life longer than seven days without water. The average man is made up of ninety two percent water in his blood. A person can be in quite a pickle without enough water. For like a car, water is the cooling system of our bodies that maintains us miraculously around the 98.6 degrees in temperature. It also is the means, by which through the blood, all the life giving nutrients are supplied to the body.

**Water gets a rating of #3.**

### *Now for AIR.*

No human being can survive longer than ten minutes without air. For in air, as is well known, we get oxygen. Every cell in the body requires this life giving substance in order to operate. Air gives the quality of combustion or fire to the body's ability to convert food into the kind of energy that runs our bodies we've all come to know as being called calories.

**Air wins the # 2 slot.**

Now, for the #1 slot. . .

### SUNLIGHT

Who would have guessed sunlight is that important. Without sunlight, there is no air to breathe, no water to drink, no food to eat. Basically, there is no life at all without our sun giving us the power that comes from light. No wonder throughout various religious beliefs the reference to light is so dominant.

With this little enlightenment on our humbling dependence for outside sources of power to sustain our life, let's take some time to consider...

## ***How Do We Get Energy To Live?***

We don't normally plug ourselves into wall sockets to get energy or stick batteries on our backs. That's because as living beings we go about getting our energy differently than mechanical machines.

All things in nature operate by getting energy in the same way; by taking in a source of energy and converting that source into energy that the body can use in order to sustain life. We call that process. . .

### Metabolism

Every living thing **metabolizes** sources of energy to sustain life. We eat food, drink water, breathe in air, and absorb sunlight in order to metabolize and produce energy for our bodies. Our bodies can do this because all these things have energy in them. Our bodies have the amazing ability to know how to draw the energy out of them. That's metabolism.

***Metabolism***

Converts Food, Air, Water, and Sunlight

into

ENERGY !

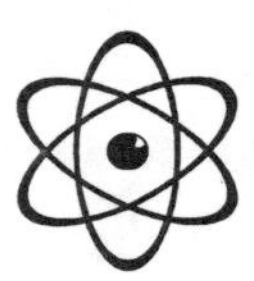

Sometimes we use up more energy than we take in, like spending more money than we have in our checking account. Then we are overdrawn. Then we somehow need to find some more money and make a deposit. It works the same way with our bodies. We eat more food, drink some more water, breathe some more air, and maybe go outside and play or work under the sun to replenish our energy bank account. When we lose energy throughout the day our bodies have a way of automatically calling upon us to replenish what energy has been used up by making us hungry or thirsty or in the desire to take a deep sigh to get more air. That urge to get outside that shows up as house-a-tosis, or cabin fever, is a physical call for the need to get some fresh air and sunlight. In response to these kinds of calls we take action to take in more energy sources and metabolize them.

Then there's a mysterious process to help metabolism do its job to restore energy. It's not a source of energy which is the topic of this chapter but an important part of metabolism so I'm bringing it up. That process as we all know it is called **sleep**.

## Restoring Loss Of Energy

Ahhhh. . .wonderful sleep! We all know about sleep, even though we may not get enough of it or get the right kind of sleep. The body and mind need rest in order to recuperate.

We sleep because when we do so we can recuperate by its transforming ability to restore new energy that we have used up and lost during the day. Sleep is not an energy source, but it sure deserves a rating like the others do. Possibly a tie with water for position #3. For if we go more than one week without sleep, the results can be fatal or at the least can be emotionally debilitating.

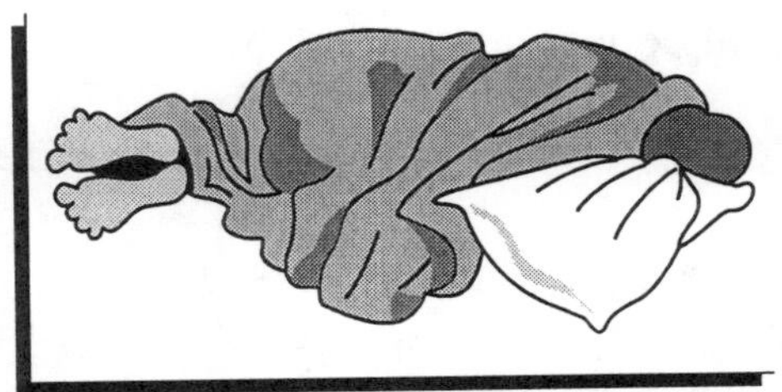

Sleep we do naturally without having to think about it, just like eating, drinking, and breathing, in order to take in energy to self sustain life. Actually, sleep or good rest is the only way we can really get back on our feet again. That's the time the body can use to take and store the new energy sources so we can get up and have the energy to be active the next day. Speaking of active, the next energy generator at our disposal is something a lot of us end up not paying much attention to, and that is. . .

## Exercise

Those who like to exercise heavily like professional athletes understand that it's not exercise that builds muscle, it's sleep. Now isn't that something? Yep. Exercise breaks down the muscle tissue but sleep is the activity of the body that repairs broken tissue. In the case of repairing exercised muscle tissue, new tissue is built and we get bigger muscles.

Exercise also generates energy. When muscles are exercised the action of movement creates a friction of tissues that produces electricity in the body that helps to keep us in action. All healing is electrical in nature as you'll discover in the physics section. So get out there and exercise!

God has made such a wonderful system in nature to keep living things working and going according to cycles. A time to work, a time to play, and an in-between time to rest. So after a day of work, grab a bottle of water, get outside in the sunlight and take a nice walk, then eat a hearty meal and end your day with a good night's sleep. Whatever your condition is you'll be living out a day towards better health.

## Definition Of Health

Good physical health is when everything in our bodies is working up to par. All the sources of energy that we have taken in can be used to sustain the natural function of our bodies at their optimum levels. In medical terms, this state of good health is called. . .

### Homeostasis

Homeostasis is the natural state of all living things to stay in health by working toward the ***balance and flow of energy*** that is drawn in to the body through food, air, water and sunlight.

1. *Flow* of Energy

2. *Balance* of Energy

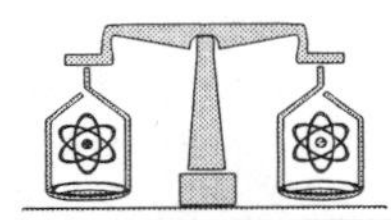

## ***What Is Sickness And Disease?***

When we are *not* in good health, we are in the opposite condition of homeostasis; a state of being *out of balance.*

When our bodies do not have enough energy to sustain themselves or for some reason can not apply that energy effectively as needed, then our bodies begin to break down. We call this process. . .

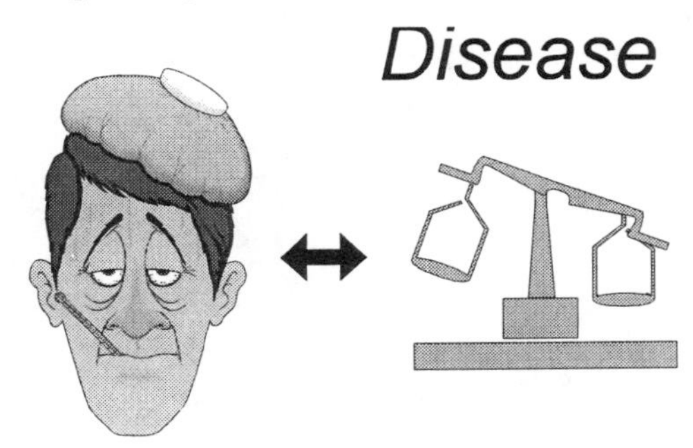


### Degeneration

If we don't eat the proper food, our bodies cannot convert the essential energy we need from the food. We become undernourished. The organs of the body cannot sustain their normal working condition and start to fail. If we don't breathe enough air or the proper air, our bodies cannot get the oxygen they need to maintain energy and we lose the strength to metabolize the food we take in. If we don't drink enough water our bodies respond by drying up or dehydrating and the electrical impulses our bodies use to send signals can't get through as easily. With all these energy sources, if we drink the wrong kinds of fluids, eat the wrong kind of foods, breathe bad air, or not get enough sunlight (or too much) we can poison our bodies. We loose the fighting strength to stay well and become slaves to sickness.

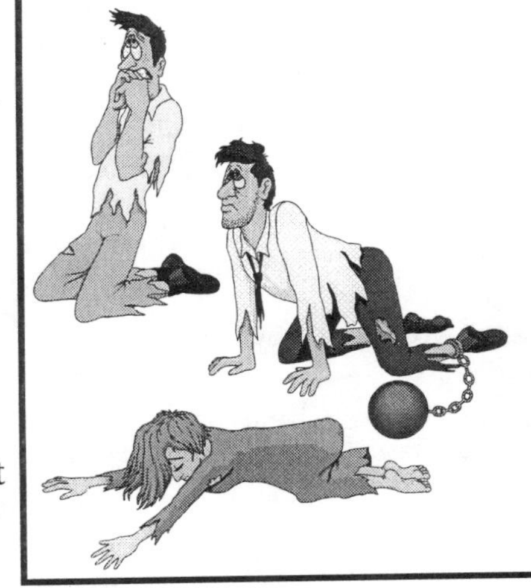

There are other ways we can get sick. An outside substance that gets into our bodies that doesn't belong there, we all know as a **virus.** In some cases, the wrong kinds of other living organisms that are incompatible with health, grow in our bodies. These are called **bacteria.** (Some bacteria is needed for digestion.) Any one of these conditions will result in a breakdown of the body's ability to function properly if we don't have the power to overcome them. We call this condition ***sickness*** or ***disease***. The amazing power of our bodies to fight against disease, virus, and the breakdown of health is called. . .

## *The Immune System*

It's the job of the body's **immune system** to guard against harmful virus and bacteria that invade our bodies. The immune system's strength is based on our ability to keep a balance and flow of the energy that flows through our bodies. When it is not able to do this the condition, in simple terms for our discussion, is called a. . .

### Block

When something gets in the way of the flow of energy to any part of the body that keeps that part from having enough energy to work according to specs, that is a ***Block***. An example would be too much cholesterol or fat in the veins. I know, there's too much talk about cholesterol these days, but it's still a worthwhile example because we've all heard about it. So, let's talk about it.

Too much fat in the veins keeps the body from moving the blood through the body. As you know, blood carries life through us. Blood carries the nutrients that every cell, organ, muscle tissue, and bone in our body needs in order to work right. It's like a river with trees on the bank. Trees rely on the flowing water through the river to supply water to their roots. Our bodies work the same way. If not enough blood gets to the heart, it can't pump nourishing blood throughout the body where it's needed. Then those organs get undernourished, for blood carries all the life giving nutrients to them throughout the body.

What happens if not enough blood gets to the head? We can't think right. The brain is undernourished and underpowered and it can't work right. It can't send its signals to give orders to the rest of the body functions so they can work for us correctly. Remember how the blood is made up of ninety per cent water? That's how the electrical signals from the brain can communicate with the body. If the signals can't communicate properly we can get confused. The electrical commands flow through the water. So you can see another reason why drinking enough water is so important to your health.

Anything in our lives that can block the flow of energy throughout the various body systems keeps us from natural good health. The energy we do have cannot get through or around the block depending on how big it is. Blocks can be other things as well, besides the example of fat, such as emotional blocks. Fear is a good one. Fear can inhibit us from doing something good for ourselves that we need, like a fear of love. Fear that hangs around too long causes tension in our bodies and causes our muscles to tighten and squeeze up preventing the flow of energy to get through. So being able to relax is significant in helping to assist our bodies to maintain balance.

Another block that is pretty simple really, but hard for most of us to overcome is eating right. Proper nutrition is vital to good health. You've heard the saying "You are what you eat." Consider our discussion on metabolizing food to get the energy out of it we need. If we eat or ingest something unhealthy for our bodies, we will metabolize it to use its energy. That's what our bodies do. However, in this case we would be metabolizing poison to our physical system. That poisoned energy gets in our blood, which circulates to all the bones, tissue, and organs including, our brains. Research has shown that improper eating habits alone can be the cause of many of our diseases such as arthritis. Many who have food allergies know what this means. Hippocrates, the father of medicine said, "Let your food be your medicine and your medicine be your food." So eating right, which is beyond the scope of our discussion for the moment, is essential to laying a foundation for good health.

There is another way we end up not having enough flow of energy to our bodies and that is what I call a. . .

## Leak

When the body has a condition anywhere where energy can escape, that is a ***leak***. Just like a leaky faucet we can leak energy.

A cut is a physical example we all can see. Get a cut; you leak blood. The natural healing process sends the stuff in blood we need to the area to seal the leak, to clot it, so we can get on with healing. A leak can be compared to a gas leak in a car's gas line. A gas line gets weak and pressure buildup creates a hole where the gas eventually leaks out, leaving you stranded as always in an inopportune moment. So with us, if we leak energy we end up losing power to keep moving down the road.

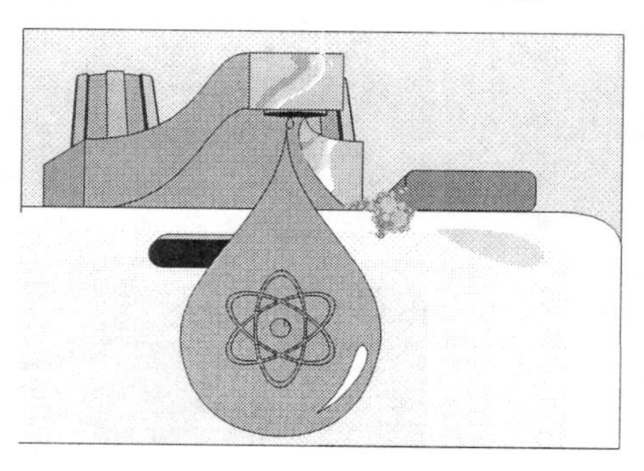

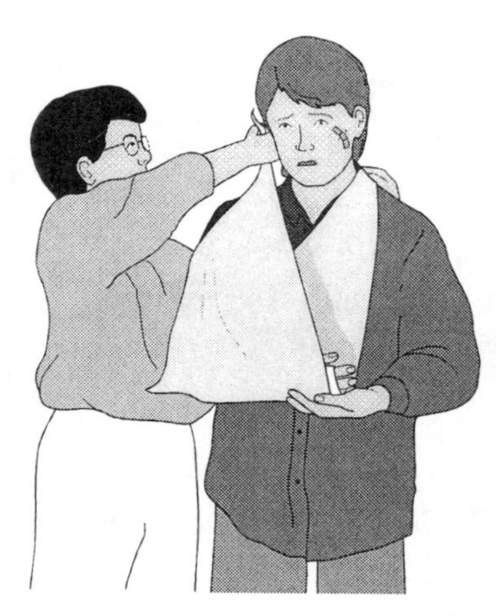

Another example would be a broken arm. The natural flow of energy is interrupted and escapes at the broken ends. The body then directs efforts to seal the leak as part of the healing process. That's a leak being sealed.

So if we suspect through various symptoms which gives clues that we have developed a leak or a block in our lives, how can we reverse the process?

## Breaking Through Blocks

As we have discussed, blocks are obstacles to the proper balance and flow of energy that is needed for an area needing nourishment or help in case of a wound or injury. The strength or size of the block will determine the amount of energy that can not get by.

Cholesterol in the veins can be so built up that it can completely close off the flow of blood. Then the energy carried by the blood is slowed down to a trickle or completely closed off. Today, surgery has been used to either clean out the vein or by-pass it all together by rerouting the blood flow through another vein. That's what we all know to be as by-bass surgery.

Blockages need to be removed by a force that is stronger than the block, either by surgical removal, medication, correcting attitudes, better nutrition, exercise, adequate sleep or anything else we may come across that can help remove it.

## Sealing Leaks

Applying more energy to make a connection between one end of a broken bone to another would help to re-establish a flow of energy. If the body has enough energy, the body can do its job to heal the bones. If there is plenty or an excess of energy to spare, there will be enough energy for the body to do all of its other natural jobs while healing of an area is going on. If there is not enough energy then the body needs to be assisted to get more to keep up. Wave Therapy is a way you can assist another person to receive, or draw in a fresh supply of energy.

## What Can Be Done?

Our part is to get the body back in a state of balance or homeostasis so the body can do its job to recover. When in balance the body can use the energy power it has metabolized from food, air, water, and sunlight that is restored through exercise and sleep. To stay in balance we have to *find* the blocks and leaks, and bring in more of the power of life to help maintain the proper flow of energy. There is a way in nature that shows us how to do that for ourselves and for others to restore the balance of power within our bodies. It's really quite a simple thing to do. That's what this book is about, to show you how to do just that.

To best understand how that process works it will be good to take a look at another part of nature that exists. For when we better understand what is going on in nature, we can better understand ourselves. Because like all other living things, we human beings are a part of nature. We will that a look at that part of nature in the next chapter, but first to recap this section.

## A Summary

- **Energy** flows around us and in us all the time that gives us the power of life. We recognize this energy normally in where we usually get it from through food, air, water and sunlight. They're ***channels of energy***. Our bodies know how to take energy from these sources of energy and use it to run our bodies. That process is called. .

- **Metabolism**. To maintain health the body naturally seeks a condition of the balance of the flow of energy called. . .
- **Homeostasis.** The body can sometimes develop hindrances to health that prevent the proper flow or balance of energy that are called. . .

- **Blocks or Leaks**. Blocks or leaks that prevent the ability of the body to remain in balance or harmony where degeneration of health occurs is called. . .
- **Sickness.** Sickness and disease are a result of the breakdown of the body's ability to repair itself and the immune system's inability to fight off harmful bacteria and virus.
- **Wave Therapy** assists in breaking through blocks and leaks of energy that the body requires to maintain health. It helps to assist the body to regain lost energy and to help regain balance and harmony that the body naturally seeks for good health.

Balance

Homeostasis

## A Look At What *Causes* The Balance Of Power

Did you know there is another natural ability within you that is responsible for how energy has the ability to flow in your body and to maintain balance? There is. It's a mysterious force that everyone is familiar with but something that we don't usually give much attention to. It's in everything and surrounds everything in existence and clues to its nature are not far away. We will now find out what that force is.

I could say it's right before your eyes, or under your nose. . .but that's a bit too close to see for now. The best clue is a bit further away. We're going on a tour, and our first stop is to take a look at a big example that's right under your feet.

Is that a good enough hint? We may still be a bit too close so let's get a further-out perspective. Let's take a bird's eye view from way up above us to see what the grand scheme of things. A view of earth from space.

So get your flying imagination going!

# Physics

## The Study Of Nature

# Physics And Health

## *The Study Of Nature*

### The Power Of Healing In Nature

We are now going to have a class in Physics. Don't worry! This is going to be easy, just like the first part on Biology. Well, maybe a little more complicated, but I'm sure you can handle this.

PHYSICS
( Physis )
Study of Nature

I'm bringing this subject up because in having a better understanding of **why** things work the way they do, I could accomplish better results with Wave Therapy. A discussion on physics is a benefit to you because Wave Therapy is based largely on what you'll find out here about the Earth. How the awesome Power of Life that is displayed in nature effects your life and health.

So, here we go!

## *Our Amazing Earth*

### How We Hold Together

Everyone knows the Earth has a ***North*** and ***South pole***. Most of us at one time or another believed Santa came from one of them. I haven't a clue what story goes with the other pole.

Anyway. . .these poles have a ***positive*** and ***negative*** quality to them. You know about them, too. If you have ever held or seen a compass you know that this little gadget has an uncanny ability to point its needle in the right direction of North and South every time.

- One end points to the North pole, and
- One end points to the South pole.

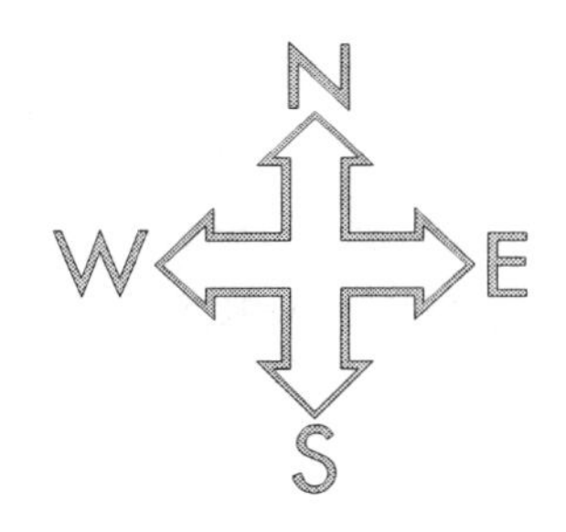


It's able to do this because the metal in the compass has the ability to respond to the ***magnetic current*** that surrounds the Earth, drawing or repelling the points of the needle from or to the North or South poles. That's pretty strong stuff to do that, wouldn't you say? A little bit of metal moving around because of invisible forces in the air.

The magnetic current that causes all this action flows in two directions that have been labeled as having ***both***

- ***positive*** (+) and
- ***negative*** (-) influences

just like a magnet does. Not many of us usually think to compare the Earth to a magnet. But, that's what it is.

And a very big one at that.

**North**

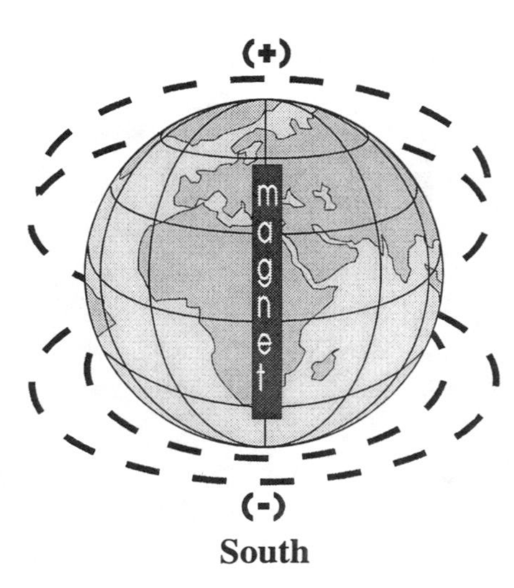


**South**

## Magnetic Fields And How We Get Them

These positive and negative influences move in and out, up and down and all around the Earth moving through and around everything. This current is generated by the motion of our Earth turning in space. It does this by the Earth's inner core moving in one direction and the Earth's outer surface moving in the opposite direction. The two motions together create both electrical and magnetic waves of energy, which is called the ***electromagnetic field.***

In practicing Wave Therapy like similar practices throughout history, people often experience an electrical quality that is felt on their body. In part what is being felt are waves of electrical energy that moves through the body. Magnetism and electricity go hand in hand. You don't have one without the other. Everything in and around the Earth is inside and effected by this electromagnetic field. That's why magnets are magnets because everything on the Earth works under the influence of this giant magnet. The Earth is a great big giant electromagnet in the heavens. So if you didn't know that, you do now. You're standing on a magnet.

Now that you get the picture of the Earth as a big magnet let's get to a smaller view of something we can get a hold of with our own hands to examine a little more closely. A little gadget we're all familiar with that displays the power of magnetism just like the Earth. The magnet itself.

## ***The Magnet***

Since the Earth is a tad too big for us to examine up close, we can use a magnet to get an idea on how all this magnetism stuff works.

(+) MAGNET (-)

It's wonderful that we have magnets. For the small little magnet that you can hold in your hand has invisible forces working in it that correspond exactly to how the Earth acts, only smaller in ability.

So, if you like, go to your refrigerator and gather up your magnet collection (or your neighbors, or go ahead and imagine with the pictures) for a bit of scientific discovery. Pretend you're back in grade school.

## A Kid's View

We've all played with magnets at one time or another in our lives. I remember being fascinated with them. When I was a kid, I remember a restaurant I used to go to called Bob's Drive In. Bob the cook, who made the best hamburgers would have these square magnets all over the hood above the grill, which he would use to hang the orders. I was always curious about how they could do that. Being a curious kid, as most kids are, I wanted to have some of those magnets to play with myself. The mysterious quality they held alone was enough to want to have some around. I asked Bob how I could get some of those magnets like his? One day he surprised me with a box full of them. As you can tell, I never forgot ol' Bob.

Magnets can be playthings that can make for hours of childhood fantasy fun. It didn't matter to me then how the mysterious force in them made them work, just that they did. Historically though the force of the magnet was seen for more than a toy. To get an idea of what that meant to people of yore let's take a look into a story about a boy and his sheep.

## Where The Magnet Came From

The story told by some is the first magnet was discovered by a shepherd as early as 80 BC. A Greek shepherd (some call Magnes) who lived in the land of Lydia in an area called Magnesia. Today it's called Turkey.

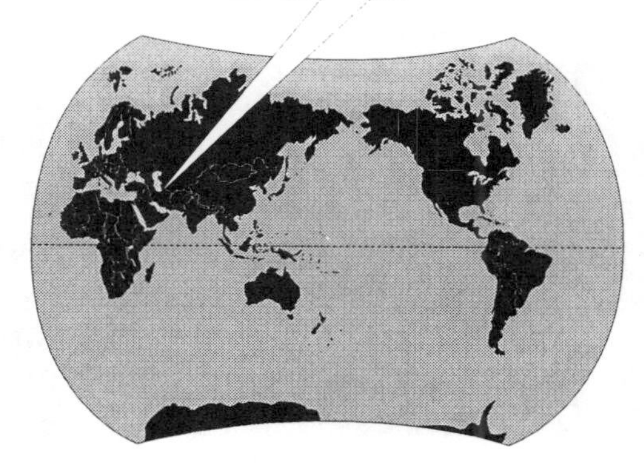

While out shepherding his sheep one day a strange thing happened. While strolling along on watch of his herd, suddenly his metal tipped staff got away from him being suddenly pulled towards a rock and just stuck there. Imagine his surprise! Tried as he may he couldn't yank it loose. So, he tried to get some leverage by holding his foot against the stone while pulling on his staff. Amazingly his sandaled foot stuck against the rock too! His sandals had iron nails in them. (Which our shepherd didn't then know was the cause.) Freeing himself from his sandal he ran to his village to tell of his story and get some help.

No one could explain the phenomenon so the people believed the rock must have had a soul, which at the time was the only way they could explain its mysterious powers. Others speculated the force (what we now know as the magnetic force of magnetized metal) was due to two spirits; one to attract and one to repel.

They called the rock Magnes being from the region of Magnesia. Thus the term magnet as we know it today.

Actually the history[4] of the magnet can be traced to many other cultures who lay claim to the discovery. There are those in other traditions that the magnet or lodestone, which the magnet was named from later, was discovered centuries before the town of Magnesia was built. But chiefly this story has remained the unofficial, official stand of history.

[4] The natural magnet, lodestone, was known in India, China, and Persia thousands of years ago. The name "magnet" is also believed to be from the Persian word *mag* which is the same word for magic, an attribute believed to signify the priesthood or Magians. The stone was then called "the Magian Stone" or the "Magic Stone". (Mind Power, William Walker Atkinson, pg.122)

Even today as adults we can play with magnets and still be somewhat fascinated by what they can do. We don't have to know how they work to enjoy them and their many uses. But, for now we are going to take a look at what makes those little playthings work. For in them lies a magnificent quality of nature that can show us the way to understanding how our health works. This bit of news will lead us to how to apply what your learn here in Wave Therapy to assist yours and other's health.

## What Makes A Magnet Work?

Magnets do have powerful forces at work. The force is not from little ghosts or magical powers as we would daydream about as a child or as people did centuries ago who didn't know how they worked in their amazing ability to attract and repel objects. But due to modern technology we've come to understand that the influences come from the Earth itself.

We can witness the power of the Earth as the magnetic fields surrounding the Earth move through the magnet.

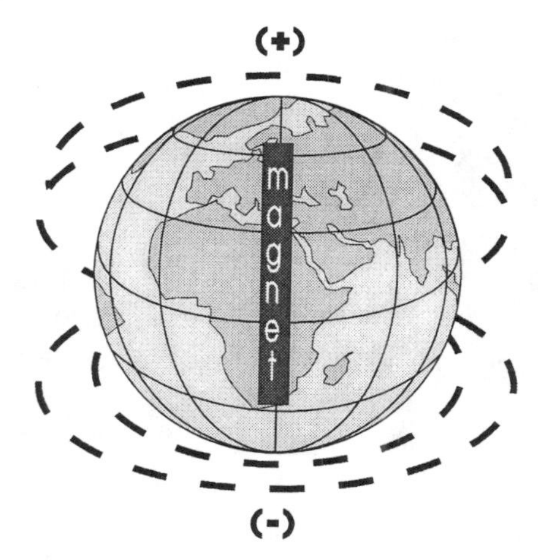


The attracting and repelling abilities of the magnet are due to the magnetism around the Earth that runs through the metal that makes up the magnet. Just as a compass needle responds to the influences of the magnetic current that flows to and from the positive (+) and negative poles (-) of the Earth a magnet does the same thing because of the metal that makes up the magnet.

### Everything Is Magnetic

In fact, everything on Earth is magnetic in some way because of this magnetism.

A pencil, a piece of string, a book, a flower, even an elephant all experience the magnetic influence of the Earth because they're inside the electromagnetic current. Everything is also magnetic all in a world of its own.

An elephant doesn't have rocks sticking to his legs as he wanders about because he is made up differently. The difference is that he and the rocks aren't made up of the combination of metal or metals that allow the effects of magnetism to be seen in action. Iron does a good job of it. We can actually see iron magnets displaying the power of our magnetic Earth.

If you have a couple of magnets handy, you can follow along with this lab experiment, if you're a kid at heart.

## Opposites Attract

If you put two magnets together, end to end, you can expect one of two things to happen. Everybody's done this at one time or another in their life.

The magnets will either stick together or repel each other. Any one who has played with a couple of magnets has made this discovery. In school, we found out the reason behind this action. If the two ends are of the same influence such as two positives (+), they will repel each other.

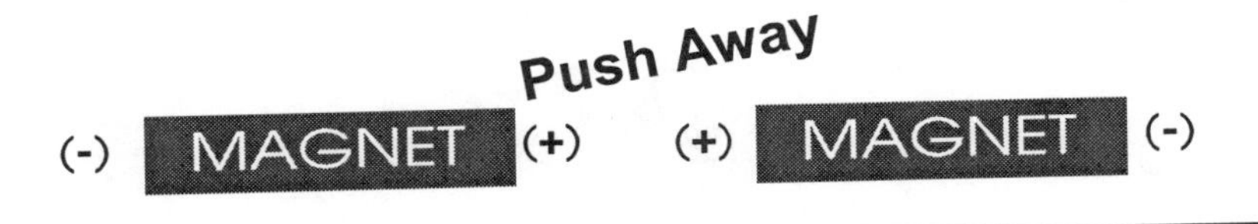

If the two ends happen to be giving off the different or opposite influences of positive (+) and negative poles (-), they will stick to each other. Sound familiar? The old "opposites attract" line? Well, it certainly works that way in the romantic world of magnets.

It can be quite a mystery why this attracting and repelling action happens but we do know basically how it works. On the Earth, these two magnetic poles keep a flow of energy moving around and through the planet. That flow, as we have learned is called the electromagnetic current. Interestingly each pole has its own purpose. Those differences are the reason behind why there is an attracting or repelling action going on. One pole **Pushes** and the other pole **Pulls**.

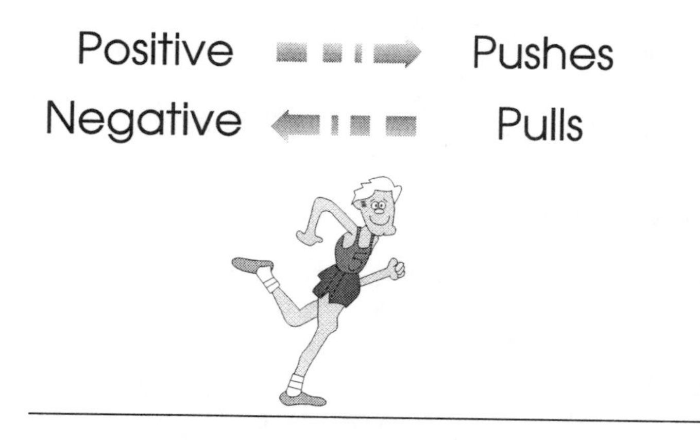


## Pushing Against The Grain Or With It

- The positive pole ***pushes*** energy and
- The negative pole ***pulls*** energy

This pushing and pulling ability of the poles work in harmony with each other to keep the flow of energy moving evenly in a nice circular motion. This is the quality of magnetism that keeps everything in balance. This balance of power between the two magnetic poles has a name that means the same thing as the balance or equilibrium called homeostasis we find in the biology of health; the ability of our bodies to seek balance from the energy we get from food, air, water, and sunlight. This balance of energy in the physics of magnetism is called. . .

**Polarity**

- The positive end of a magnet is labeled (+). It's positive in polarity.
- The negative end of a magnet is labeled (-). It's negative in polarity.

Everything in nature has this ability, from the Earth and the planets that circle the sun itself to the unseen workings of the atom.

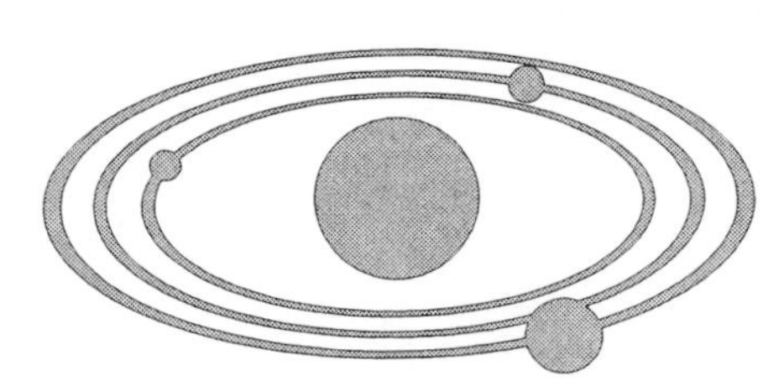

Everything in existence has a positive (+) and negative (-) pole inherent in its nature to keep things in balance. Pulling in energy that flows by magnetism from one direction and pushing out the energy in another, all in a nice circle.

How's the brain doing? Hang in there! The hard part is behind you now. Well, just about. One more major thing to go over and that's to find out how and why your body exists. . .in physics anyway.

The how's and why's of physics discussed here are not about the purpose and meaning of life but to find out how that body of yours holds together. To understand that, we're going to have to go smaller than a refrigerator magnet.

## An Imaginative Trip

We started with the Earth, then moved to something smaller with magnets and now we're going down still further to take a look inside your skin. So hang on!

For your guide in this trip you'll need to invite your imagination along. Think of using your eyes as a pair of lenses of a powerful microscope.

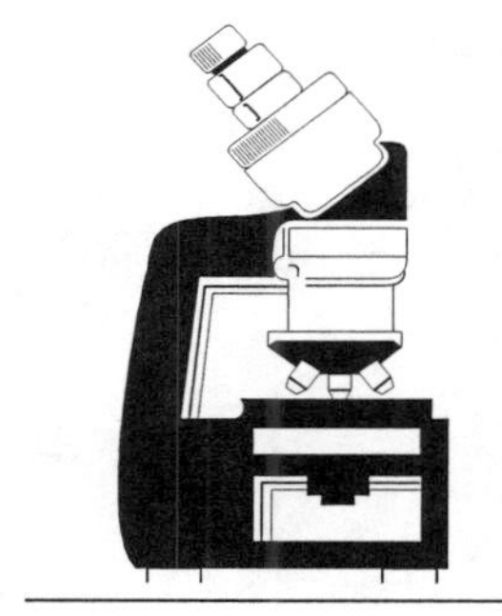

After you've taken a look at say. . .the skin on your arm, use those super peepers of yours to imagine you're looking down into the cells that make up the skin you see. There are millions of them, five hundred trillion in fact. Now use your imagination to pick out a couple of cells and enlarge them enough to take a look at them.

Here you are. . .two cells.

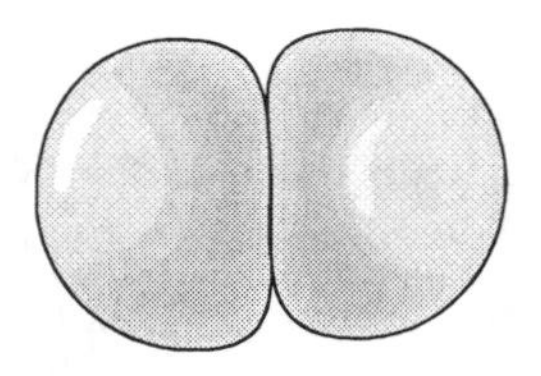

Now just as you went down through the skin you're going to take a ride down farther to see what makes up a cell.

## The Iddiest Biddiest Thing In The World

You know about atoms. They're the little iddy-biddy energy things that make up everything. If you could look through a powerful enough microscope, you would see them all swirling around. Now's a time for a good question like. . . 'What's all this got to do with magnets. . . or with me?' Here's why. . .

## Even Atoms Are Magnets

The thing about magnets is that the atoms are all organized to move in one direction. One end of the magnet has the atoms moving in one direction, the other end in the opposite. That's how you get that push/pull effect when you put the ends together of a magnet. All the magnetism found in the Earth is flowing through the magnet in one direction or the other. The metal in a magnet is what makes it able to do what it does in drawing or pushing things away from it, causing it to do what it does in picking things up, like a paper clip and why elephant feet don't.

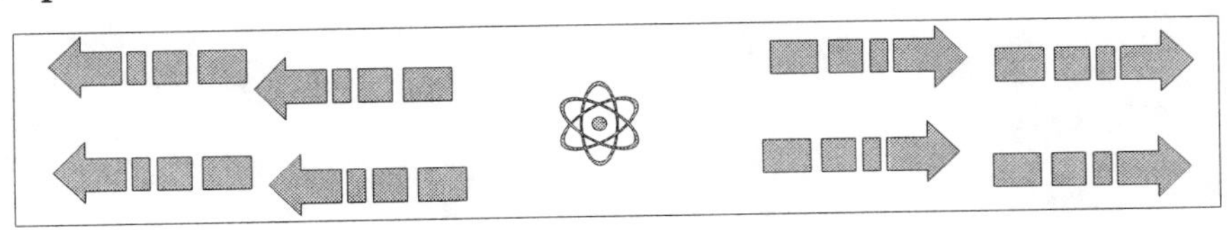

The same magnetic atoms are in elephants but organized to move differently than in metal magnets. They're organized to move in different directions. They follow a pattern of elephant-atoms so you don't have a zebra instead of an elephant when they stick together.

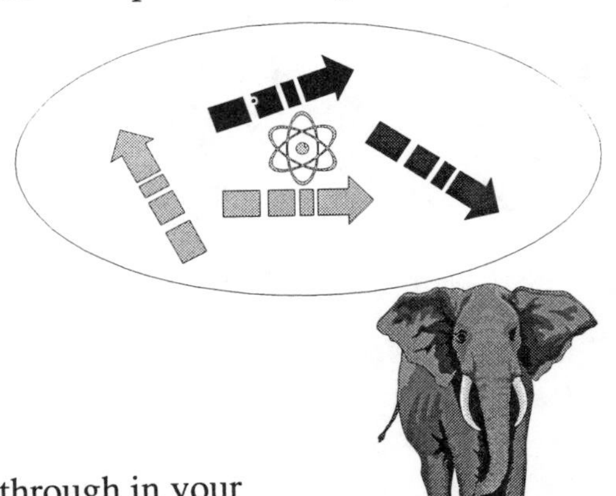

## Moving Up

Now it's time to ride back through in your imaginative romp to start seeing bigger again. Now that you've seen the atom and how it works and how they can stick together to make a cell, lets see what happens on our next stop on the journey.

Atoms work the same way as magnets and the Earth. When you get a lot of them to stick together, they make up what you'll find on our next stop in getting bigger, what we all know to be a . . .

### Molecule

A molecule is a collection of atoms that have attracted themselves to each other. . .like magnets. Whaddya know, more magnetic stuff! They can do this because they are swirling bits of positive (+) and negative (-) influences that attract and repel other molecule atoms. Pulling together the ones that are like each other and repelling others that aren't. Working just like two opposite ends of a magnet put together.

That's how we get skin. A bunch of like-minded skin atoms get together and when enough of them get together they form into something bigger, making skin molecules.

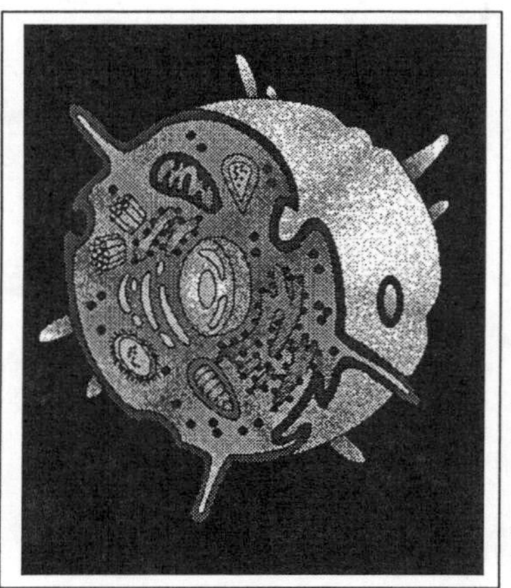

It works just like a few guys who get an idea to form a bowling team. A few hopeful league developers bring the idea up and get together with enough other interested guys and end up with a team. Skin molecules act just like a group of eager bowling buddies wanting to get together; eventually you have a enough pulled together to make up the cells that become the skin.

And the same goes for every other part of your body like your liver, your bones, the heart and so on.

Everything in nature works this way, not just our bodies.

### Magnetism Holds All Things Together

Magnetism is the power that enables everything we know of in creation to bind together to bring about physical existence as we know it. It's a magnificent process of creation. I like to think of it as God's way of using power creatively. An imaginative way of expressing divine Will for all things to hold together. There's a verse in the Bible that says, ". . .in him all things exist." [4] So, if you like, one way to think of the physics of magnetism is as a scientific expression of God's creative will that keeps all things in balance and in wholeness.

[4] Colossians 1:15

Without magnetism, we would have chaos. No stars circling in the galaxy, no planets circling the sun, no moons circling planets, no planets spinning in space, no atoms circling in motion, pushing and pulling, holding themselves in place. Magnetism is a great power that holds all things together.

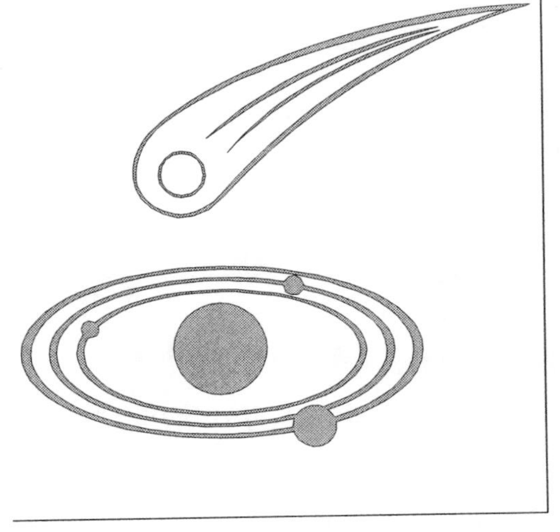

## The Trip Back Up

Now that we've looked at magnets a little bit, let's take a look at another magnet with which you're real familiar. So reverse that imagination of yours, reverse the direction of your microscopic eyes, and ride back up from the atom to the cells, through the cells, move upward and pass the molecules to the surface of your skin. Then move on out a little farther and take a look at yourself.

## People Are Magnets Too

Yep, just like the Earth, you have a north and south pole. A negative (-) and positive (+) quality to you, and not just meaning your personality.

Like everything else on this Earth of ours, we take part in magnetism too. Just like how the Earth keeps the flow of energy within and around it, your body acts the same way as a magnet does. Even though we don't walk about with arms waving around pointing to the north and south poles of the Earth like a compass does, our bodies still are influenced by the magnetic field.

That's because magnetism can flow through anything. Even though we don't usually see it (some people do) it's there just the same. Like we don't see air. It's there, though we don't see it. . . usually. . . unless you live in L.A.

Now we're going to discover why this little study of the physics of magnetism has to do with understanding how Wave Therapy works to assist in healing.

## Your Magnetic Anatomy

### The Body's Magnetic Poles

Like the magnet and every other thing on Earth, the body has the two poles of polarity that are positive and negative. Just like a magnet's *strongest influence is at its two ends*, the body works the same way where overall:

- **The top of the body is positive (+)**
- **The bottom of the body is negative (-)**

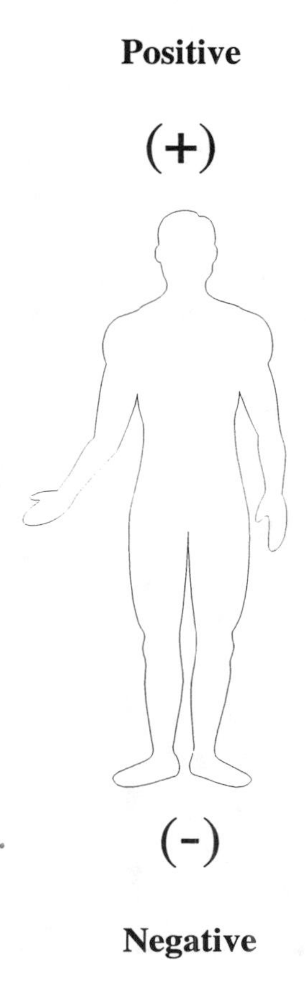


### Two Sides

Just as there is polarity on the top and bottom side of us there are the sides to consider.

The body has all kinds of places where it's positive or negative along with the top and bottom of the body.

We're going to stick to the information here that has to do with working Wave Therapy where the. . .

- The left side of the body is Negative (-) and
- The right side of the body is Positive (+)

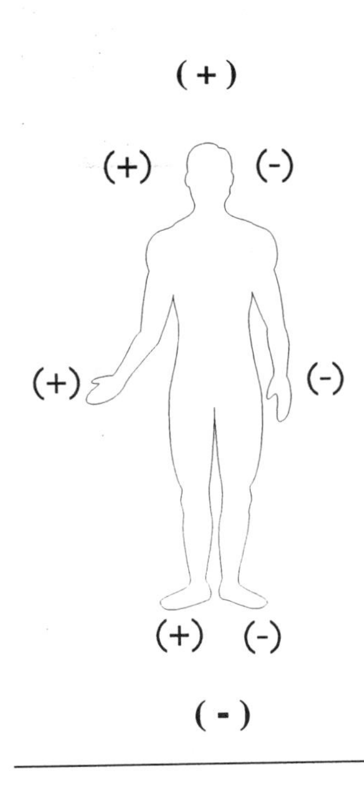


As we have discovered, the push and pull effect of the polarity of magnetism keeps energy flowing in a circle. Let's see where that leads us.

## The Flow Of Energy

In the laws of physics the electromagnetic current flows

***from*** the positive (+)
***to*** the negative (-) pole.

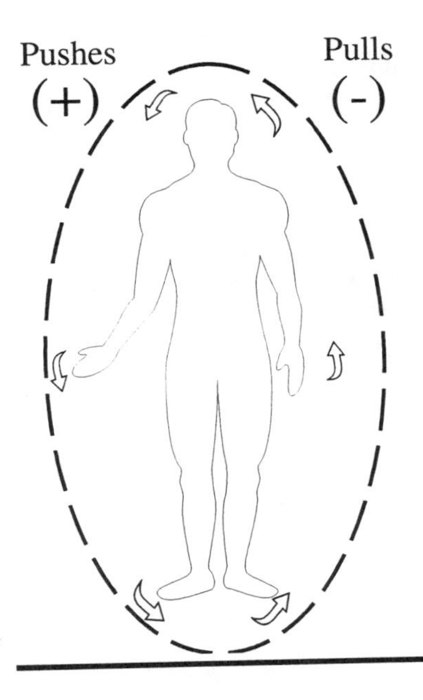


The power of life flows along the lines of magnetic current where the energy comes in one direction into the body and flows out the other.

- The positive pole (+) ***pushes*** energy from one direction and
- The negative pole (-) ***pulls*** energy in the other direction.

*Positive* magnetism (+) ***pushes*** energy from the right side and negative magnetism (-) ***pulls*** energy from the left side.

Magnetic energy can also do this from the bottom of the body down below the feet. . .

- Pulling (-) energy in up through the middle of your body toward the head ↑
- Where at the head the polarity switches and becomes positive on the back side,
- Pushing (+) energy back down towards the feet. ↓

Everything in nature does this, from the Earth itself to the unseen workings of the atom. Everything has a negative and positive pole inherent in nature. Pulling in energy from one direction and pushing out energy in another all in a nice circle. Now for the BIG question?

Why?
My Only Answer: It just works that way.

### Your Positive And Negative Hands

So to move you further on your way to understand how you can help others to heal is to find out something more about yourself. Since your left side is negative and your right side is positive,what follows is. . .

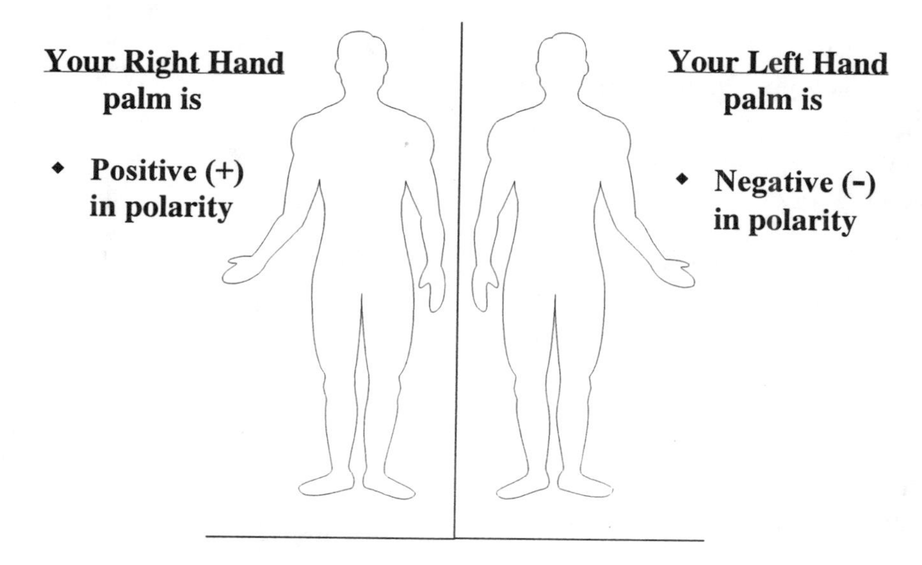

## Why Are The Hands Important?

Wave Therapy is based on the principle that the hands are highly magnetic in nature. The end of any magnet is its strongest point, the weakest at the center. So it is with your hands as being at the end of your arms. They are the strongest ends of the flow of the power of life that flows along the magnetic lines of energy that runs in and out of your hands. The head is also a strong point as well as your feet for they are also at the ends of the body from top to bottom.

In the oldest from of healing known through out every culture before modern medicine there was the shaman, or medicine man. In that culture they presented the understanding that power came in and out at the top of the head.[4] We will discuss later how to work with the various ways energy flows through the body through its channels of several magnetic areas. Our focus for now will be on your hands.

- Your hands are what you will be using for Wave Therapy sessions to effect another person's magnetic balance and flow of energy.
- With your hands you can effect the positive and negative flow of energy that manages a person's health.

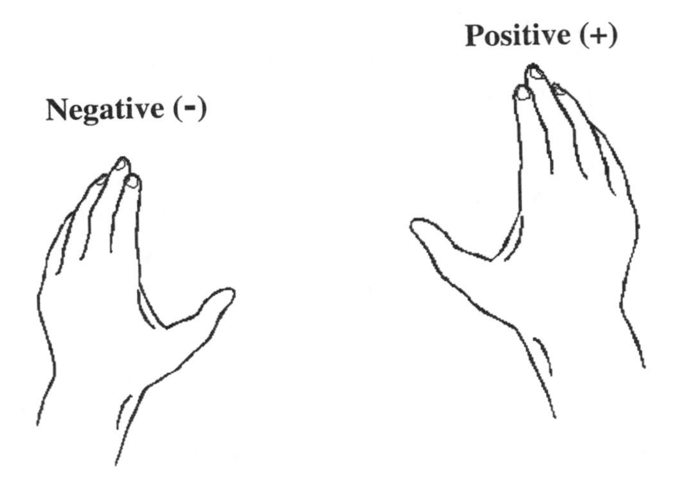


4 At the "soft spot." For those schooled in body anatomy it's called the fontanelle where the temporal and occipital bones meet at the top of the head.

### You First Step To Know How To Help Others Heal

Before learning *how* to apply negative and positive energy through your hands we are now going to take a look at the different effects positive and negative magnetic energy have on all living things. When applying Wave Therapy you'll have choices to make about what *kind* of energy is needed and how to apply it. You will need to choose between applying either:

- **Negative energy (-) (left hand) or**
- **Positive energy (+) (right hand)**

Each kind of energy has specific purposes and will effect the body differently. Both influences have effects on the body (and the mind) that are as different as night and day. Choosing which hand to use will be easy to figure out once you learn the differences as you will soon discover.

## *Positive And Negative Influences*

The words positive and negative in magnetic language don't refer to good or bad actions. The terms refer to the actual influences negative or positive magnetic energy have on living systems.

So far you've learned about all the positive and negative stuff, but not how their influences work or what that has to do with health or in assisting others to heal. To understand which hand to use we're now going to take a look at what the different influences of positive and negative energy can have in your life.

### The Effects Of Negative Energy

Negative energy overall causes reduction of stress in our lives. The less energy spent on overcoming stress leaves more energy available to stay strong. The amount of negative energy in your body will determine how well your system has the strength to overcome an infection or work toward healing an injury.

Some of the effects of negative energy are to:

- Decrease pain
- Arrest growth of bacteria
- Arrest growth of viruses
- Relieve stress and strain (emotional as well)
- Strengthen cells
- Increase alkalinity
- Increase perception
- Improve circulation of oxygen in the blood (Blood is negative or alkaline overall)
- Manage the central nervous system

## Some Conditions Effected By Negative Energy

Some of the conditions you can expect to effect in using negative energy in Wave Therapy are listed next.

- It reduces swelling, viruses, bacterial infections, pain relief as from arthritis or injury, increases oxygen content in the blood, fluid movement, dissolves calcium deposits in joints, attracts white and red blood cells to injured areas, reduces fat, and encourages sleep and rest.
  Negative energy helps a person to become more mentally alert and clearer thinking by helping to relieve stress.

- Some of the attitudes associated with negative energy is our ability for healthy reasoning, thinking, sensibility, being an understanding person. Negative influence protects, affords health; controls emotions and helps us to be more closer to our natural being.

## A Familiar Experience Of Negative Energy

You may have heard of the reason people feel better when they're around the ocean? It's because of the negative influence of the molecules in the air caused by the motion of the waves of the water. There is something that happens to the air in which **negative ions** are produced which makes us feel better, rested, inducing a pleasant state of mind. You've heard of or maybe used negative ion machines? The machine charges the air with negative magnetism around you which helps to give that soothing relaxing effect as when you're at the ocean.

As you can see from the list of goodies that are associated with negative energy, it would seem that most of us could use more.

Now for the positive magnetic influences.

## The Effects Of Positive Energy

Positive energy overall causes a stimulation of body activities toward growth as with the brain, spine, skin, muscles and bones. While negative energy normalizes and calms our body systems, positive energy *increases* them.

Some of the effects of positive energy are to:

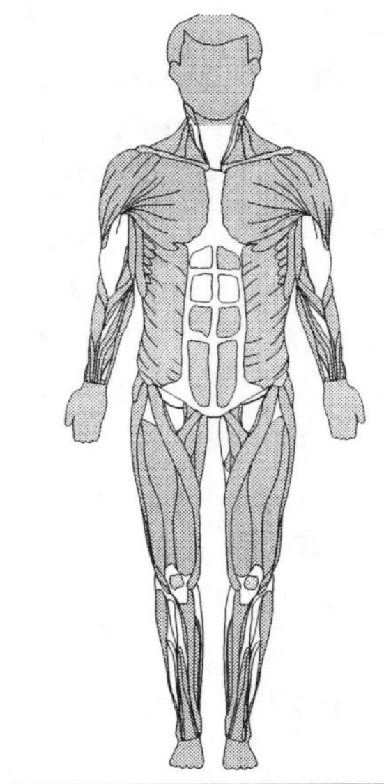

- Cause growth and development
- Increase energy and vitality
- Increase physical strength
- Increase acidity in blood
- Stimulate thinking
- Stimulate wakefulness

## Some Conditions Effected By Positive Energy

Some of the conditions you can expect to effect in using positive energy in Wave Therapy are listed next.

- It strengthens muscles, limbs, joints, tendons, ligaments, increases blood flow and circulation, strengthens glands, organs, and production of fluids.
- Attitudes that are considered positive in nature within people who have an overabundance of positive magnetic energy are those who are more ego minded, less concerned with the rights of others, fight peace, order, harmony, and generally unhappy, unreasonable, inconsiderate, and insensible people.[4] Positive Air Ions stimulate a rise in emotions and general feelings of unrest, uncertainty, confusion and anger.

## Pain, Stress, and Positive Energy

When we experience pain in any area of the body there will be found an overabundance of positive energy. Applying negative energy will help reduce the pain.

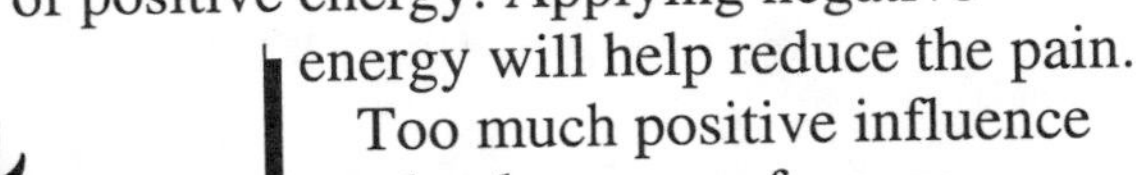

Too much positive influence can be the cause of worry, nervous reactions, anxiety, headaches, loss of strength from overuse, aging, inability to sleep. Positive energy also encourages growth of infections caused by bacteria and viruses. Bacteria and virus are positive in polarity. So that's one of the reasons you

[4] (Magnetic Blueprint of Life, pg.101)

need to know the difference between the different effects of positive and negative magnetism.

**Overall what is needed is more negative energy rather than positive**

Too much positive energy (stress) is what's responsible for most human illness.

### You Have The Tools

Pretty impressive list of stuff, isn't it? It's interesting how not only do our physical bodies but our attitudes, even an outlook on life, are woven into our being a part of this wonderful creation we live in.

Now that you understand how the two magnetic influences are a part of our lives you can get a better glimpse into understanding what's going on with a person to help someone in applying the therapy you are now going to learn about.

You can see there is a lot of good you can do for others if you just knew how to do it. Wave Therapy gives you the tools to assist the balance and flow of the power of life within every cell of your body that moves along the lines of force of magnetism.

That's what the next part of this book is about, showing you how to apply the healing power already available to you that's built into nature to bring balance and harmony in all living things.

## Review

I've presented some of the effects applying positive or negative influences can have on someone. They are quite different from each other and as we have seen it's helpful to know their differences in order to give you a guideline on what hand to use when you run across a health problem someone or yourself needs help with. Next I'll show you how to apply your hands to get the results you're looking for.

Now for one more look the different influences your hands can have on the energy fields of those you work with.

## Your Left Hand - Negative (-), What It Can Do

- Overall causes reduction in activity and strength (too much positive) in the biological system.

The amount of negative energy in your body will determine how well your system can overcome an infection and injury.

Left Hand

- So you will use the left hand any time there is a need to decrease pain, fight infection or disease, cause relaxation from relief of stress, such as needing to sleep better. For if we return to our list of effects of negative magnetism we will find that the negative influence of the left hand. . .

- Decreases pain
- Arrests growth of bacteria
- Arrests growth of viruses
- Relieves stress and strain
- Strengthens cells
- increases alkalinity
- Increases perception
- Improves circulation of blood (Blood is negative or alkaline overall)
- Ease tension

## Your Right Hand - Positive (+), What It Can Do

- Overall causes the building up a physical strength of the brain, spine, bones, muscles, and skin.

Right Hand

We need positive energy for personal vitality. Too much positive energy in the body represents too much unresolved stress in life that leads to a breaking down of the body's system rather than strengthening it which can lead to sickness and disease.

You will use your right hand whenever a person is low on energy or weak. Since positive energy stimulates growth, where ever there is pain, you generally don't use the right hand for it will increase the pain. You will use the negative energy of the left hand which decreases pain.

The positive influence of the right hand:

- Causes growth, development
- Increases energy, vitality
- Increases physical strength
- Increases acidity
- Stimulates thinking

There you have the two different influences that your left and right hand can have on a person's body and health.

Now we'll take a few moments out for a summary of what was covered in this and the last section to pull all this together before moving on to how you can apply your hands to help others in their health.

## Summary Of Biology And Physics

Magnetism is the power that enables all physical things in nature to hold together. The power works that way because it has two magnetic influences of positive and negative poles of polarity that either push or pull things together or away from each other. This push/pull effect is what makes the atoms, the building blocks of all physical matter, join together to make up everything that you see and feel. Without magnetism holding all things together, things would not only fly apart, but nothing physical would exist in nature to be seen. In other words, there would be no eyes to see anything that wasn't there. How's that for a brain twister?!

Magnetism is also what is responsible for the ability of our bodies to maintain the biology of homeostasis, keeping all things in smooth working order within our bodies. This process is responsible for every working mechanism in our bodies including blood circulation. Without the push/pull effect, for instance, of your heart there would be no blood flow in and no flow out. Everything in nature demonstrates the push/pull, positive and negative, character of magnetism.

The energy we take in from food, air, water, and sunlight travels along the lines of the field of force surrounding and flowing through the body. This power of life needs to be kept in balance and harmony for us to stay healthy and well.

There are different effects both positive and negative energy have on and within living systems to maintain harmony and balance. The negative calms and soothes, while the positive strengthens and builds. To influence another person's energy field the left hand will apply negative energy while the right hand will apply positive energy.

## Onward

The next section will show you exactly how to use the negative and positive effects of the magnetic flow of the power of life that flows through your hands to assist others in their body's natural healing process. The ability is already there and the simple hand positions you'll learn can be used anywhere at anytime to help with many common health problems you and I face throughout every day living.

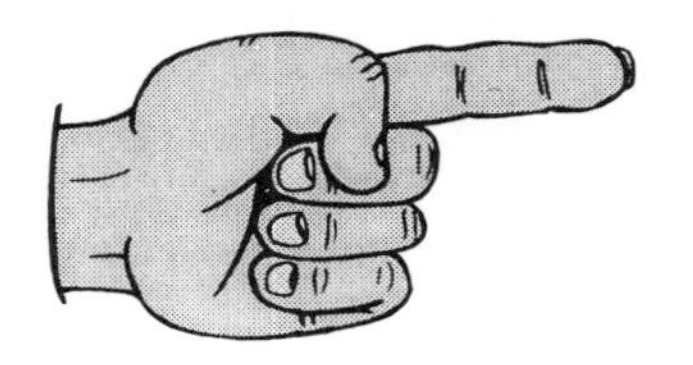

When the whole of the scientific[4] and medical communities begin to respond as they seem to be headed, that the human biological system is both magnetic and electrical in nature and treat it as such, a new wave of development of our health system will emerge. Until then you can be at the forefront of modern medicine to be, by practicing Wave Therapy.

Now we'll see what that's about.

[4] Many notable scientists today are making that move such as Robert O. Becker, M.D., who believes there to be one fundamental force that heals; electromagnetic energy. See The Body Electric, Electromagnetism And The Foundation of Life, Robert O. Becker, M.D., and Gary Selden

# Part 11

# Wave Therapy

## How To Do It

# Wave Therapy

## How To Do It

### Review

(Review or in case you've jumped to this section ahead of the others.)

We have had an overview of some simple laws of nature. If we follow or align ourselves with the laws of nature we reap the benefits of good health.

### Biology

In biology the ***law of homeostasis*** is the natural tendency for all living things to seek and maintain the proper balance and flow of energy to maintain health. When we follow the rules of proper nutrition, sleep, rest, and exercise we assist our bodies to draw in and metabolize these sources of energy that promote good health. If we break those rules, that serves to block or leak the proper flow of energy, we reap the results of disease and sickness.

### Physics

There is also natural law of physics that seeks for the proper balance of two opposite poles of magnetic influence that's common to all living and non-living things. These positive and negative poles serve the purpose of holding all things together to maintain the proper balance and flow of energy, whether it's the earth, a rock, a tree, and atom, or our human bodies. This balance of the two poles is the ***law of polarity***. When polarity is misaligned, or out of balance, we experience a condition where energy metabolized for the power of life that fuels our bodies does not flow properly.

### Health

When our bodies cannot use the energy available or do not have enough energy to do their work, we cannot keep up with overcoming infectious disease or have the strength to promote repair from injury.

These conditions are caused by blocks or leaks of energy. Removing blocks and sealing leaks assists energy to move in its proper balance and flow. Then our bodies can be empowered to move themselves back into a state of homeostasis and healing can be the result.

## The Goal

The work of bringing the body into balance and harmony is the goal in all work doctors attempt in their practice of medicine. No doctor or medicine can heal. They only assist the body to get into a condition where the body can heal itself naturally. Therefore, there is better health available for everyone through the use of taking personal responsibility in supplying the body with healthy energy that comes from proper nutrition, sunlight, air, exercise, and rest.

Wave Therapy does not treat disease or offer cures. What it does do is offer the skills to assist in the:

1. **Increase of energy, and the**
2. **Balance of energy**

Wave Therapy seeks to assist a persons ability in gaining strength to naturally overcome disharmony and imbalance of energy that is reflected in the symptoms of illness and injury.

## What You Will Learn

What I'm presenting here is nothing new. Today, even though we better understand the physics and biology of how our environment functions in magnetic and electrical wave currents, the same concepts have been accepted and used for thousands of years only with different names. I'm sure that the concepts we've discussed are nothing new to you, as well, just that some of the more obvious things may have been overlooked. Now is the time to show you how to put your knowledge to practical work.

→

# ***Five Techniques***

I will show you **FIVE** non-touch hand techniques to get you started on the road to assist others in their healing process. They have, in my experience proven effective in helping others to stimulate their own body's self-healing system. Your hands will act as natural tools to release and move the power of life that is governed by the laws of magnetism as it flows around the earth and through you and the person you work with. In this chapter you will learn how to choose between which hand positions best suit the needs of the person for simple health complications, and in the next chapter how to combine all the positions for the benefits of whole body Wave Therapy sessions.

The Five hand techniques are:

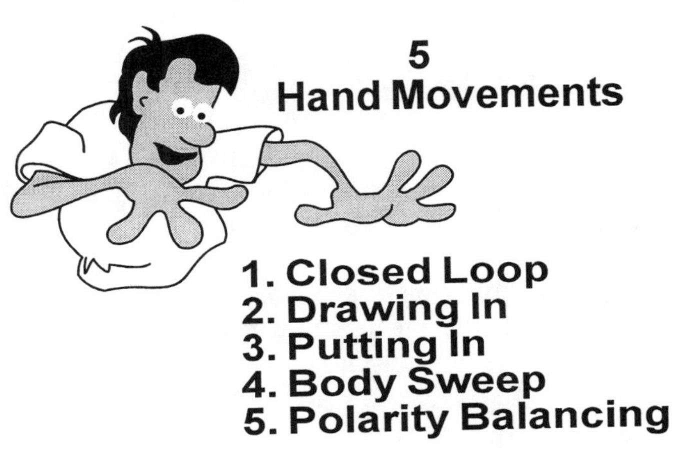


That's it!

We'll go over:

- **How to do each one**
- **When to use which one for different health complications and**
- **Why the use of any one position can affect your health**

## Some Health Complications To Expect Progress In

In using these hand positions, I've seen recovery from various blood disorders, organs replace themselves in their correct positions, scars dissolve, severed nerves repair, colons and intestines clean themselves, tumors dissolve, bone structures move back into proper positions, chronic pain disorders like arthritis and Fibromyalgia diminish, joint damage repair, headaches disappear, sinuses clear, emotional disorders balance, emotion from painful memories be released, calcium deposits and burrs dissolve, and many others.

For more serious health complications, discipline will be a key in making progress. The body, if in severe health disorder, will simply require added attention. For instance, a common problem we all go through at one time or another is the pesky "cold." I've found if you apply a Wave Therapy session at the onset of the symptoms of a cold, one overall whole body work-up (next section) will nip that puppy in the bud overnight. If you wait until you're way into the cold, it will take more time and attention, for the body needs more energy from the amount lost in trying to keep up with efforts to overcome the problem. So don't give up if you don't see "miraculous" recovery instantly from one try. Hang in there! The power at work behind the principles of Wave Therapy is powerful and effective if you follow through with determination.

The techniques or movements are very simple. Once you learn them, try them out on someone and see what happens. Something will. I have yet to experience one person who hasn't benefited to some degree by using one or a combination of all these movements.

## I know you can do this. You can't fail at it!

Why am I so confident? Because every living human being has energy moving through them. This energy is moving through you at this very moment. Everybody does it. This powerful energy is what keeps us alive and going, the energy of the power of life.

So, let's get started!

## Meet Your Energy Field

It's time to give you your first glimpse into an awareness that from this moment on can change your understanding of life as you have previously known it. Pretty good promise, huh? This can happen when you discover for yourself the reality of your own ***energy field***, and the power of life that flows through you along the lines of magnetic force. If, you have experienced this before, this may be old hat to you. If so, lets experience it again. You may have experienced this sensation before but not known what it was.

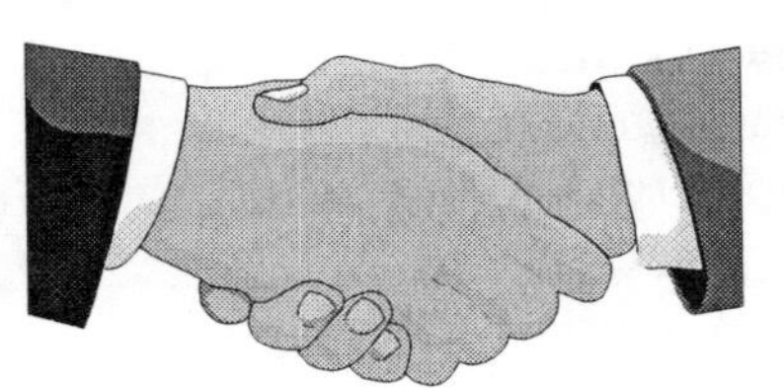

## Hold Your Hands Facing Each Other

- Simply hold your hands, palms facing each other about 2-6 inches apart, or whatever distance feels comfortable for you.
- Hold them there until you start to feel something.

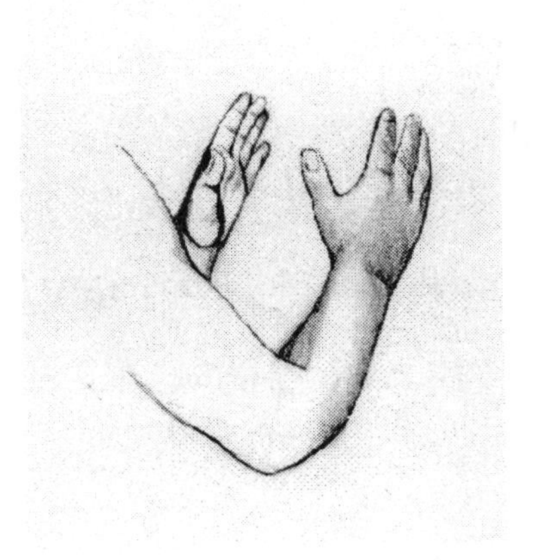

What you will experience will be revealed on the next page.

**Don't peek for the answer!**

Put the book down and experiment first. Hold your hands apart from each other and wait to see what happens.

Did you feel. . .

- A growing sense of warmth? Or,
- You may experience a sense of tingling in your hands.?

Either way that's it! You are experiencing the flow of energy that moves through your body. In this case it's energy flowing from one hand to the other. You may even feel something like a pressure build up between your hands, somewhat like holding a ball or a balloon. If so, that's it!

What's going on is the circular motion of waves of positive and negative magnetic power of life flowing in a loop between your hands passing from one to the other.

If you don't feel the sensations of the movement of energy right away. . .

- try rubbing your hands together briefly in a brisk circular fashion like you're warming your hands over a fire.

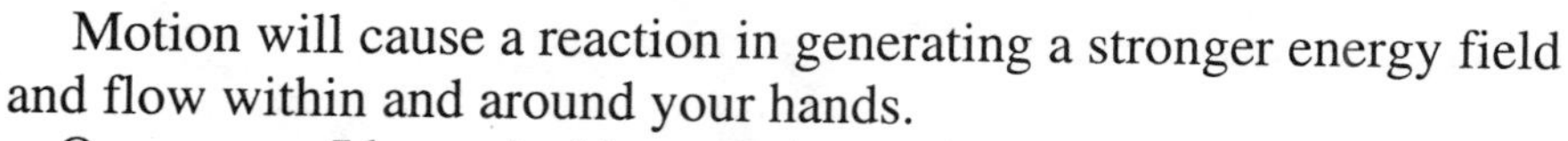

Motion will cause a reaction in generating a stronger energy field and flow within and around your hands.

One person I know had been trying to feel the energy with no success for quite some time. After I suggested rubbing his hands together he instantly could feel the change. Once you get started it's like riding a bicycle, you never forget how to do it.

## It Works Whether You Feel It Or Not

If you have done this exercise and you don't feel anything, this doesn't mean you have failed. It means you simply haven't felt the energy yet. It's there or you wouldn't be standing. It's a part of that power that keeps that heart of yours ticking and gives your legs the power to stand you upright. Hang in there because you will feel it eventually. When leading people in this exercise I make it a practice not to let on to anyone what to expect. I wait till they speak up about what they feel. This way it helps to answer the question some may bring up that they're imagining the sensations. Whether you feel any energy or not makes no difference in being able to do Wave Therapy. On my first try at this with someone I didn't feel anything but the healing results happened anyway. The action of magnetic electrical power of life is still moving through you regardless of whether you feel it or not.

## Two People Exercise

Here's another way you can sense energy flow of the power of life.

- Stand opposite someone.
- Hold your left hand up like you're making a pledge facing the right hand of the person opposite you who has agreed to hold their right hand up.

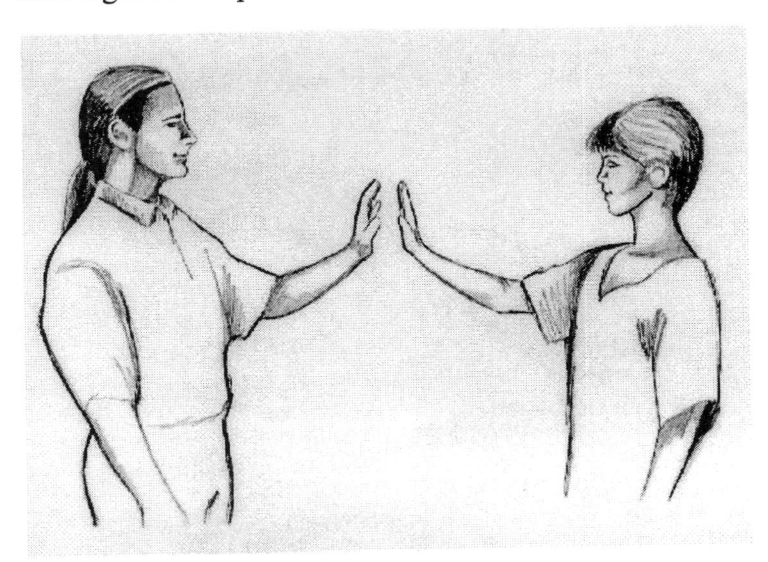

You may feel silly doing this but it's worth the experience.

- Focus your attention on the palm of your hand. It helps.
- Wait

Again you may feel a sense of warmth or tingling sensation. You are intermingling your energy fields together. If you don't feel anything, hang in there; you will before you finish doing all the movements you'll learn here.

Sometimes when I work this experiment with people, I often don't feel anything in my hand while the other person does. If you still don't feel anything after working these two exercises don't despair by believing there is no energy there or you're the one rare person who can't feel anything or there is something wrong. There is nothing wrong. All this says is "you haven't felt the energy flow." Be patient. With practice you will.

I didn't feel anything in my hands on my first experience.

### My First Experience

With my first experience in practicing Wave Therapy I didn't feel anything at all. But, the effect was there, regardless.

When I discovered that there was this process going on in my body (as I told you about in chapter one) I was a bit reluctant because I felt kind of foolish telling my friend that holding my hands around her knee could do anything to help heal her of her condition. But, I agreed to try. After all, I brought it up. And I was interested to see if it really did work.

Today, Mary Jo doesn't have to have knee surgery to have her knee replaced.

That's an example of what can happen with this therapy. And you know another thing? At the time I didn't feel a thing in my hands. The power is there and available. The first thing you have to do is try.

## *The Basics*

Now we'll get down to the basics of how you can assist another person to increase the flow of energy and build up his or her natural healing abilities.

There are:

- **Three still hand positions and**
- **Two action hand positions.**

### The Three Hand Positions Are:

1. **Closed Loop**
2. **Drawing In**
3. **Putting In**

### The Two Action Moments Are:

1. **The Body Sweep**
2. **Polarity Balancing**

This chapter will show you how to use the first three positions, two of which are used the most. The two you can use anywhere at anytime are the Closed Loop and Drawing In. Putting In will be used primarily for whole body work which will be covered in the next section. There you will learn how to use the other two action movements, the Body Sweep, Polarity Balancing, plus Putting In, to include for extended whole body work

## *The Two Hand Positions To Assist In Most Healing*

If you go no further than this chapter, you'll come away armed with two tools you'll most often use to assist others in their health.

### Two Primary Hand Positions

The two most common positions you can use (and can do anywhere) are the:

1. **Closed Loop** and
2. **Drawing In**

These two hand positions are very effective for almost all the regular aches and pains people experience. (Animals too!)

They're good for helping to:

- Relieve pain from broken bones, cuts and bruises, headaches, arthritis pain, joint pains, any pain or general health complication you may experience through everyday living. They will also,
- Assist growth in areas such as broken bones and torn ligaments to accelerate the healing process.

You can do these two positions while riding on a bus, waiting in a movie line, or eating out at a restaurant. The only thing holding you back is any self-consciousness you may have of people looking at you in a curious manner. Personally, I've found that people tend to pass on by with hardly a glance.

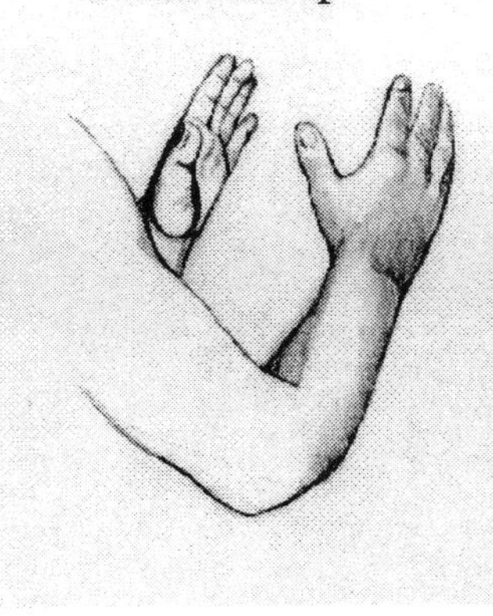


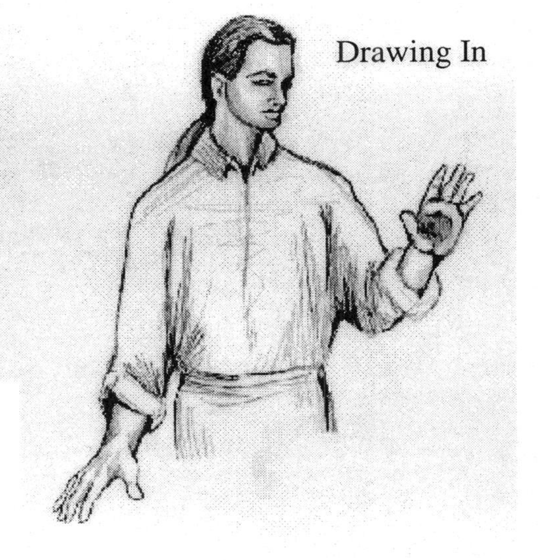


Now will move on to:

- How to apply each of these positions
- Why each position works magnetically
- What they positions can accomplish for better health and
- A few stories of uses with various common health problems.

The first position you can use for almost everything is choice. . .

# #1

# The Closed Loop

The Closed Loop uses both positive (+) and negative (-) magnetic influences of the energy in the power of life.

### The Hand Position:

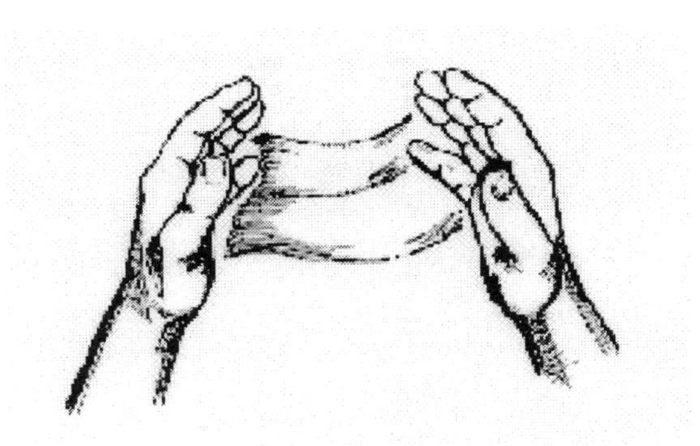

The Closed Loop is done in the same way as described in the first lesson of attempting to feel your own energy field. So you already know how to do it!

Here it is.

- Hold your hands parallel to each other with palms facing.

That's it!

### How To Apply The Closed Loop

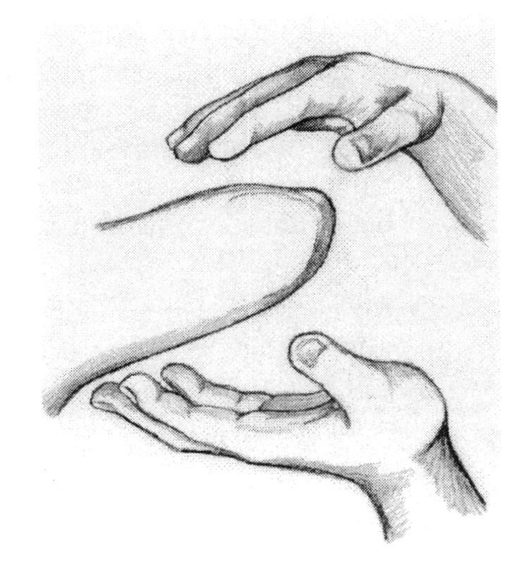

Simply hold your hands in this position with any body part between them. Like an elbow, wrist, knee, or hand. The distance that works best for you is found out through experimenting. It can be different for everyone. Start with one to three inches. Sometimes it could be as far as twelve inches more or less.

Ask the person you're working on how it feels to them. If they feel it to be comfortable or feel a warming or tingling sensation you have found your distance. Then again, they may not feel anything at all to begin with and you're the one feeling the sensations.

There is another option open. . . neither one of you feels a thing. If this ends up being the case at anytime maintain the distance with one to three inches, and wait. Something will happen eventually.

When holding this position on someone you more than likely will feel a stronger sense of tingling in your hands. This is because the energy is passing from the right hand to your left hand within a very close distance. This position is helpful for almost any painful area.

### To Review

- Hold both hands from one to three inches away around any area of the body that hurts.

You may have expected something more glamorous, but to help others to heal is as simple as this: hold your hands around any area that hurts.

## Story

Recently my father had a terrible pain in his right forefinger. It had been there for four days before he said anything about it. It was so painful that he couldn't touch the end of his finger to any surface no matter how soft. He had confessed of this pain while sitting at his desk at work. So, I had him hold his hand out, and I held my hands parallel to his in the Closed Loop position, about three inches away from his hand, not touching them. In about one minute I asked him if his finger felt any different.

"I don't know. It doesn't feel any different. Let's see." (My Dad is one of those who doesn't feel the process at work very often. Occasionally he'll say he feels a little heat.)

He tried touching his leg ever so slightly. . . carefully, just in case he would feel pain. He touched it and in welcome surprise said,

"Why that's much better!" He could now touch his finger to a surface while hardly feeling any pain.

So I suggested we try a little longer to see if all the pain would go away. He agreed again.

So I held the Closed Loop position for a couple more minutes. After that he felt no pain at all. The next day there was still no pain and hasn't returned. (As far as I know)

The process of holding my hands around his finger was a healing act that took very little effort by either of us but had a powerful effect.

## You Can Do Closed Loop Anytime, Anywhere

This is a very simple thing you can do for someone anywhere, anytime. I even do it for people I meet at the mall, on the street, in grocery stores, elevators, anywhere someone looks as if they're in pain (displayed by casts, braces, arm slings, limps). No one has every refused help. I don't know whether it's because the surprise of a perfect stranger saying, "Hey, I can help you with that" catches people off guard that makes them act so willingly or what? But they always do.

Here's one of those kind of situations that happened which illustrates what I mean.

## Another Story

One time I entered a convenience store to get a drink. When reaching the counter to pay I noticed a clerk had her arm in a sling; the thin kind that wrapped around her wrist to hold her arm up. I said,

"What happened to you?" and she gave a quick story of the event that led to hurting her elbow.

"Does it hurt right now?" I asked.

"It sure does."

"Well, give me your elbow a second and I'll help the pain go away."

She stopped what she was doing after she had taken my money for the drink, looked at me but then swung her arm out to greet my outstretched hands, which were already waiting in the Closed Loop position.

I placed my hands around her elbow and she stood there while customers where filing around me. (This convenience store is always busy being on a downtown main intersection.)

"What are you doing?" she asked.
"Oh, it's just a way I found that helps with pain."
Silence. More people passing by us.
After a few seconds I asked,
"Well, how's it doing? Does it feel any better?"
With a smile but a curious look on her face she says,
"Yeeeeesss. . ."
"Good!" And I turn and waltz out the door. Drink in hand.

## Still Another Story

Another time I did this for someone who was helping me hand move a boat to its parking spot in our garage. We got a little ambitious pulling it forward to straighten out the angle to back it in to its spot and didn't notice a pole in the way. We didn't stop the boat from moving in time, and the tongue of the trailer banged his hand between the metal tongue and the pole. Needless to say, that hurt.

His hand started to bleed from a small cut. I didn't think any further than to say,

"Hold out your hand."

He didn't know what I was intending, but in response obediently held his hand out. I held my hands out at each side of his hand. Within a few seconds the bleeding stopped so quickly that it even was starting to dry up. His hand never did hurt after that.

You see how simple this is?

And anyone can do it. Just try it on anyone who has a complaint of muscle pain, bruises, broken bones, or any other reason for pain and see what happens. The simple aches and pains often leave within a few seconds to a couple of short minutes. Other pains that may come from more serious complications can take longer and may need multiple sessions. But no matter how long or how many times you do this, some kind of pain relief will be the result.

## Why The Closed Loop Works

The Closed Loop position engages both the:

- Calming soothing effects of the power of life that flows through the negative (-) magnetic field of the left hand and the. . .

- Encouraging growth influences of the power of life that flows through the positive (+) right hand magnetic field.

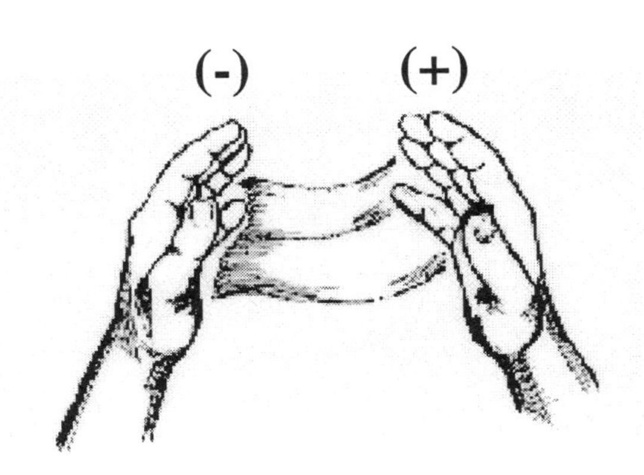


There are many health problems where it's better to use both of these two influences together of the Closed Loop at the same time, like when someone breaks a leg. You would first want to help with calming the pain by using the negative left hand energy. Then again you probably would like to be helpful in assisting their body in building up the strength of the muscles and bone tissue of the magnetic effect of the right hand. You can! By using the power available to everyone in the use of the Closed Loop.

The Closed Loop is by far the best method to work with joints. It helps both to strengthen weak areas and to ease pain.

## Use Any Place

You can use the CLOSED LOOP anywhere on the body for these results, not just on joints. For bone therapy, it's the best position of choice to gain quicker results.

The Closed Loop is a powerful movement that is very strong because it combines both energies of the negative and positive poles.

There are times when using only one or the other energies of positive and negative influence is needed. Each influence has its own effects on the human energy system.

Our next hand position will demonstrate how to use the negative side of the power of life by its self, its effects, and when to use it.

This second hand position you can us is choice. . .

# #2

# Drawing In

Drawing In uses only the negative energy of the power of life. Here's how you do it.

### The Hand Position

- Hold your **left hand** in front of you with palm facing the floor.

- Hold your **right hand** out to your right side, palm facing the floor.

Drawing In is a variation of the Closed Loop where you will use only the left hand over the body.

This is the most effective position you can do that helps the **immune system** work in fighting against disease and sickness due to bacteria and virus.

- Bacteria and virus are positive (+) in nature.
- Negative (-) energy in the body helps to fight them.

Drawing In helps to increase the fighting ability of the body to defend against harmful bacteria and virus. If we are low on negative energy, we don't have the reserves to fight off harmful germs that come our way.

Drawing In it works much like drinking through a straw. This move will assist in drawing in negative energy for the person you're working with.

You can also think of it as drawing out, as in drawing fluid up and out of a container through a straw. Those I've worked with often report a sensation as if "something is being drawn out." That's what it may feel like. I prefer to call the position Drawing In for it focuses on drawing in energy to the person rather than drawing out, which can give the impression you're depleting someone of energy. However you personally would like to refer to the action going on here's how you do Drawing In.

## How To Apply The Drawing In Position

The left hand can be held over any area that needs healing, such as a bruised knee, the head for sinus congestion, headache, cuts, stomach problems or any place on the body that needs relief from pain, viral, or bacterial infection. Hold the left hand over the area, with the right hand palm facing the floor.

Most likely you will begin to feel the tingling sensation or warmth in one of your hands. Usually the left hand but sometimes you will feel it in the right hand. The person you're working with will most likely begin to feel tingling or warmth, as well. (You may find he or she feels similar sensations in other parts of the body as well. This is common, as energy moves to the place it's needed the most at the time.)

Watch for your right hand palm getting lazy and end up aiming at the side of your right leg or foot. More than likely you'll start to feel little trickles of energy going down your leg as the energy moves from your left hand out through the right hand to the floor.

## A Story

Once again, I'm going to tell you a shopping story.

One day I was needing a minor replacement part that had gone bad on a filter pump. So I was off to the hardware store. A young man offered his assistance to look for the part I was needing. As he was rummaging through a box of stuff on a shelf he finds what I need, picks it out to hand it to me then lets go of a little whelp-of-pain sound and he starts flipping his left hand. He had some kind of injury on his index finger. It was bandaged. My cue for action!

"What happened to you?" I asked.

"I cut my finger a couple of days ago while making a key for a customer. I had to have three stitches. I just banged it on the shelf."

"And it still hurts pretty bad?" I asked. (Silly question.)

"Yes it does! The pain has been so bad that it's been running up my arm in to my shoulder. I can hardly lift my arm up in the air."

(He tries to demonstrate lifting his arm out to his side and stops about mid way up.)

"I can help with that pain," I say

"Hold out your finger!" I command gently.

(I'm amazed at people every time I do this. They are so obedient when it comes to getting rid of pain. . .and with a perfect stranger.)

He immediately sticks out his finger in front of me.

I hold out my left hand and place it a few inches above his finger and hold it there. My right hand palm facing the floor. (I kind of keep that part unnoticed off the side and behind me.)

"What are you doing?" he asks.

"Oh, I'm helping your body to do what it wants to do; to heal. I'm assisting it by drawing in some energy to the hurt area that your body wants and uses to heal."

(Small talk is good in these moments. It helps people to keep paying attention while you work with them.)

I'm silent for about ten seconds. So is he, while staring at his finger. Suddenly his eyes start to grow wide open. I know the familiar look.

"So you feel something going on?" I ask with innocence.

"Yes!. There's this. . . this. . . what is that?!"

"What is what?" (I'm terrible!)

"I feel this tingling thing going on in my hand. This is strange. What are you doing!?"

"Is the pain going away?" is my response.

"It sure is. This is the weirdest thing I've ever seen. This is incredible."

He pauses.

"That tingling stuff is moving up my arm!"

His eyes are like saucers by now. His staring at me as if I'm his personal close encounter with an alien.

I decide to hold the position for a little while longer while we're still lingering in place between the aisle shelves. Then I take my hand away and then ask him,

"Now, how is that arm?"

He slowly starts to test it by moving his arm up. He gets it all the way up to shoulder height. . . bug eyed in wonder.

"I don't believe this. There is no pain in my arm any more. Look at this." And he starts to wave his arm up and down.

"This is amazing. What did you do!?"

I begin to explain a little bit what it's about with the earth's magnetic field, while in the middle of it remember to thank him for finding the part I was needing. We continue to chat as we turn to go to the counter for me to pay for my six cent part. I thank him for a wonderful time and again for the part and I'm gone to fix my pump, leaving another person wondering what just happened to him. The whole healing adventure, in and out, was about fifteen minutes.

## Why Drawing In Works

The Drawing In position engages solely the negative magnetic effects that bring about the soothing, calming, restful energy our bodies use to recover from strains, cuts, bruises, and from disease due to virus and bacteria. The negative effects of using only the left hand can always be counted on to help the body receive negative energy to help to arrest pain and to assist the body to heal.

**All healing in the body is a result of a negative flow of electrical magnetic current of the power of life.**

## Why Use Drawing In Over Closed Loop?

Sometimes you may find that pain doesn't lessen with the Closed Loop position. If this is your experience then switch to Drawing In. The reason is explainable through the simple laws of magnetism.

With the Closed Loop you are using both the positive and negative influences of energy that flow along the lines of force in magnetism. With Drawing In only the negative influence is used. Let's compare the two positions for their different affects. Here's what you get when using the Closed Loop. . .

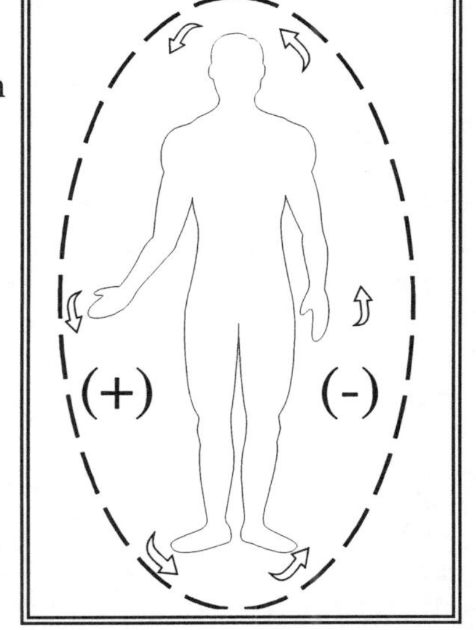


- The right hand is positive (+) and
- The left hand is negative.(-)
- Positive energy increases, causes growth and stimulation.
- Positive energy can increase pain since the job of positive magnetism is to encourage and stimulate growth, which for some can mean an increase of pain. With the Closed Loop position you are adding the effects of positive magnetic energy from the right hand therefore increasing pain.

In Drawing In here's what you get.

- Doing away with the positive effects of the right hand leaves only the negative effects of the left hand. On the other hand, (you can find a pun here) negative energy will always decrease pain.

- This position only uses the force of negative magnetic energy for those sensitive cases where the addition of positive energy is actually helping to increase the pain in an area. With Drawing in you're doing without it.

## Drawing In Is Good (Or Bad) For Infections

The Drawing In position is advisable for any area where there is an infection. Infection that is due to bacteria is magnetically positive in nature. Applying a stronger force of negative energy with the left hand will diminish the strength of bacteria or virus (which is also positive). Negative energy will also add strength to the immune system.

You might think there is a discrepancy here when I say "negative energy will also add strength. . ." since I've presented that it's positive energy that adds strength while negative energy calms and soothes. Try looking at it this way. When you are tired and you get some rest, the rest brings about the recuperation that you need to get up and go again. The rest strengthens you. That's how negative magnetic energy works. It relaxes and soothes as in the case of overcoming bacteria and viral stress on the immune system so it can gain headway to do its job to fight disease. In effect "strengthening" it.

When applying negative energy from the left hand, you are applying a force that strengthens the immune system to rid the body of destructive bacteria and virus.

## To Review Drawing In And Where Do You Place Your Hand?

- Hold your **left hand** <u>in front of you</u> with palm facing the floor.
- Hold your **right hand** <u>out to your right side</u> palm facing the floor.

Hold the left hand out over the painful area with your palm facing downward. Again keep your hand about one to three inches away from touching the person.

Hold the right arm extended out from the side of your body parallel to the floor with the right palm facing downward.

The form of this position acts in harmony with the natural flow of energy that runs in a loop through your body. The left hand acts to draw in energy and the right hand acts to draw out energy from your body to the floor.

## Hand Distance

Your hand distance from the body is a personal thing. No big rule here. Experiment with where you feel comfortable. Generally, it's when you begin to feel a tingling, a warmth sensation and sometimes even a cold sensation. At whatever distance you begin to feel one of these sensations, stop and hold there. You've found your place to begin.

We've talked about how to apply negative magnetic influences of the power of life. Now to learn how to apply positive energy, for what purposes it has, and when to do it. The final hand position you can choose from is choice. . . .

## #3

## Putting In

Putting In engages positive (+) magnetic influence of the power of life.

Putting In is the least used position. Not because it isn't valuable but by itself the power of positive magnetic energy is helpful in more limited circumstances and places on the body. Positive energy is found in the energy makeup of bones, muscle and skin tissue. So the use of Putting In would serve the purpose of adding positive energy to strengthen, build up, excite and cause growth in these areas.

Here's how you do it:

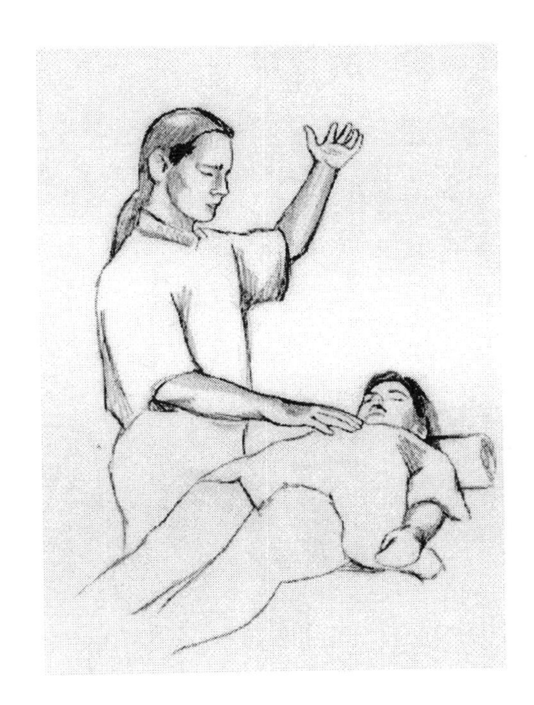

## The Hand Position

- Hold the **right hand** in front of you with palm facing the floor.
- Hold the **left hand** up in the air about shoulder height palm facing upward. Sort of like an antenna. That's what it's like.

## How To Apply The Putting In Position

The right hand palm is held over the area that needs working on, generally restricted in focusing work to strengthen bones, muscles and skin. The left hand palm is held facing upward. The Putting In position is used just like Drawing In except you hold the right hand over the area you're working on instead of the left hand.

The natural growth influence of Putting In positive energy should be limited for use in health complications where there is no viral or bacteria infection or the natural result of applying positive energy will serve to cause growth of any virus and bacteria. Negative energy from Drawing In arrests virus and bacteria growth while positive energy's natural function would be to cause virus and bacteria growth. That's why Putting In is more limited in its uses, since many common health problems are a result of immune system weakness in combating virus and bacteria related diseases. Drawing In would be the hand position of choice to be more helpful in these circumstances.

## Benefits Of Putting In

Generally I reserve using Putting In for working with two places on the body; the:

- Heart and
- Solar Plexus (Upper stomach area)

and occasionally for working with

- Skin, bones and muscles tissue

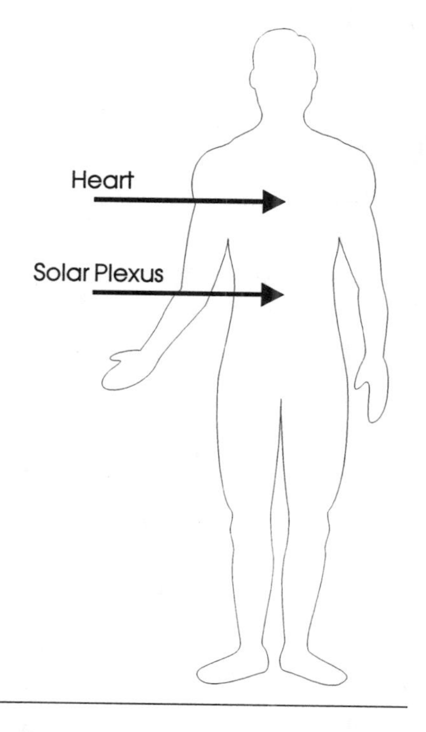


The greatest benefit of Putting In is in adding strength and vitality to the whole body system generated by positive energy. Vitality can be increased through the solar plexus area and the immune system enhanced through the heart region. Both these areas will be covered in the full body work-up section.

As a general rule Putting In is best reserved for use where there is no virus or bacteria present in a health problem. Putting In can be also be helpful in relieving pain like Drawing In where the cause is loss of strength and need of growth in bones, muscle and skin.

## Rib Story

My father had an unexpected bout of unusual chest pain. The pain must have been pretty bad for being the silent type he would normally never let on he was in any discomfort through complaining. I discovered the true nature of the reason behind his recent slower movements when he finally let out a whelp of pain one day at lunch while trying to squeeze into a restaurant booth. After a few more days of the pain not letting up we discovered from a much insisted on doctor's visit that somehow he had broken two ribs. No wonder he was hurting!

I tried Drawing In on his back and there was some release of pain. Since I use Drawing In more often in pain situations than Putting In I was slow to realize the benefits of switching to use positive energy for pain since generally the job of positive energy is to strengthen and build up. He certainly didn't need any strengthening of pain! But this was a bone problem. To be cautious I was careful to have him be watchful of any pain increase because I was going to try a different approach.

I switched to Putting In and he reported the pain began to subside, not increase. It had been two weeks since he had been able to lean back into a chair without pain. After a few minutes of Putting In he was able to lean into the back of a chair without pain. With continued daily sessions of Putting In he recovered quickly and was up and running again.

## Why Putting In Works

Here's what's happening magnetically.

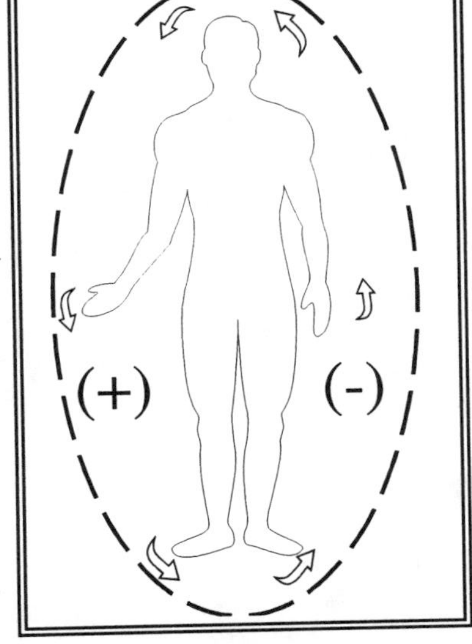


You're bringing in negative (-) energy as usual with the left hand. As the energy moves from the left to the right side of the body[8] that energy changes to positive (+) and moves out the right hand. Following the rule, the left hand is negative and the right hand is positive. The Putting In position engages the positive polarity of the right hand in nature so with this position you are applying positive magnetic energy of the power of life.

Positive energy is what we use to build up, strengthen, and cause growth. It's the energy from which we get our vitality and get-up-and-go from. Without the power of positive magnetic energy you could never get up out of bed.

[8] Or right to left depending on your point of view, since energy always moves in a circle.

## Sleep Vs Awake

When you are awake and running around throughout the day, your brain is utilizing positive energy to keep things going. At night a miraculous thing occurs when you go to bed. Just at the time of your going to sleep the brain switches its polarity overall to a negative resting mode.

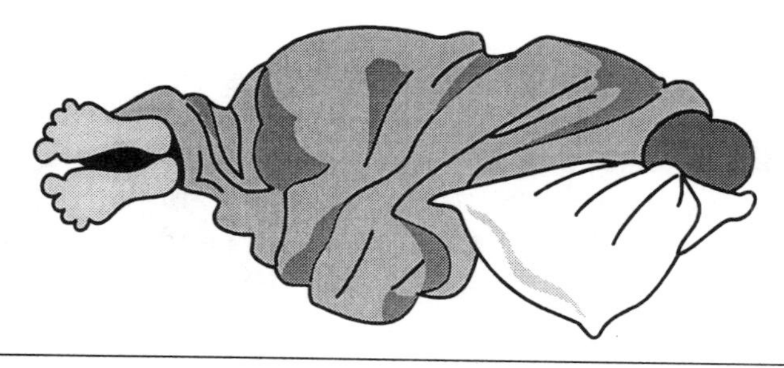

- Resting is negative (-) action
  and
- Wakefulness is positive (+) action

Thinking is a positive energy activity. So, if a person is overworking the brain with too much thinking that's keeping him or her up at night applying negative energy to the head with the left hand (Drawing In) will help calm the person down. (It also helps to add clarity to thought because it calms down overactive thinking.) This wakefulness is one reason I tend to not spend too much time with Putting In while working with people. For the most part, we all tend to be overstressed, meaning we have a lot of excess positive energy moving through our systems. Generally, more negative energy is needed rather than positive.

## More On Putting In

The positive energy of Putting In is used in the Closed Loop position by the use of the right hand but is balanced out with the negative energy of the left hand. That's why the combined energy of the Closed Loop can be helpful when used with the pain and repair work needed in broken bones, cuts, bruises, and swelling. The use of both energies together help to calm pain, healing through the repairing work of the negative energy and the building and strengthening ability of skin, muscle and bone through positive energy. They work wonderfully and powerfully together.

Since stress (+) seems to be one of the primary contributors to the breakdown of the body's self healing reserves the negative energy of Drawing In is needed more. I reserve Putting In for use during a whole body work-up primarily because during a whole body session Drawing In is used extensively which helps to balance out any excess positive energy which in overabundance appears as stress against the immune system to fight disease.

## Review Putting In

- Hold your right hand over the area, (solar plexus or heart usually) and
- Hold your left hand palm facing upward.

Applying positive energy can bring about three results:

- It can strengthen muscle, bone, and skin tissue
- It can increase pain already present, which is magnetically positive in nature
- It can give someone so much energy they will be up all night!

Now some people will welcome this last point, especially if they need to clean their house. I've had many people give me stories of their being up all night after a full session from not being able to sleep. They either get so charged from the release of tension that has been tiring them out or the positive energy they received gives them a real boost. I think it's both. So I tend to be a little more restrained with the using solely positive energy on people if they already are fairly active.

## How To Notice Enough Positive Energy Available

One noticeable result occurs when using Putting In that can offer a clue there is enough positive energy. A person experiences a growing sense of heat in the abdominal area that is rather uncomfortable. It may even last for days. Counter by using Drawing In.

# The Rules

Ahh, yes, there are always rules somewhere.

## How Long Do You Hold The Hand Positions?

Here are some guidelines to know how long to hold the use of the Closed Loop, Drawing In, and Putting In positions.

Here Is. . .

## Rule #1:

- With any hand position hold your hand(s) in position until either the tingling or warmth **goes away,**

or

- When **ten minutes** have passed.

Which ever comes **first.**

Then you can move on to the next spot to work on.

Watch that you don't get impatient here with your timing. I've watched eager- beavers in their excitement want to hop on to the next spot almost as soon as they feel the tingling. There's no hurry here. Stick with it so you can do the most good for somebody. What you're doing is assisting in bring needed energy to an area on someone who is low due to a block or leak that has developed.

I have found that rarely do I have to hold a position for ten minutes. The usual time is up to three minutes. But, in case you don't know when you should discontinue holding a position apply the ten minute rule.

## Filling The Tank Is Enough

Working Wave Therapy is much like taking your car to get gas at the gas station. You get the gas pump handle, plug it into your gas tank, pull the handle, and fill up your tank. When it's full, a trigger goes off on the pump handle to automatically shut off the flow.

Your hands are act sort of like the pump at the gas station. The person is the car that needs gas. In this case when your hand(s) tingle, it signifies that filling up is going on. As long as the tingling is going on, your hand-pump is assisting in filling the person up with energy. When the person has had enough energy, the tingling stops to show the area is now full like the trigger releasing on the gas pump handle. So no need to go on; you're just spilling over. It's time to stop.

So, follow the guidance the person's body is giving. Don't stop short and cheat the person out of getting the energy he or she needs, and don't overdo it and give more than needed.

You really don't hurt someone with too much energy in a spot, but it can cause discomfort in some. If a person begins to feel achy while filling in with energy, you can choose to back off or continue for a while to see if the pain lessens. No need to force the issue. You can always come back to it. It's better not to overdo with enthusiasm. Balance, balance, balance!

## Healing Crisis

To much "help" for someone can bring on a ***healing crisis*** for serious complications that can add unnecessary discomfort.

One of the natural rules of healing is while a healing takes place there is always a healing crisis. A healing crises is when opposing forces occur from not being in equilibrium. Remember that word, equilibrium? It means balance. Being out of balance is the cause of sickness and disease whether emotionally, spiritually, or physically. The process of coming back into balance can give off a sense of pain, as well. In these cases some pain is a sign of something good happening. It's a communication of what the body is doing. Have you ever had an itchy feeling on a wound that has a scab? That itchy feeling is the work of healing going on. So when such occurrences happen there is little need for concern. The body is doing what it needs to do. It knows what it's doing. Let it do it. You help the body do its work by assisting in supplying energy to do its job. Just don't try to do the job for the body by pushing it.

On to the next rule. . .

## Rule #2

- **Only Do A Closed Loop On The Head From *Behind* The Person.**

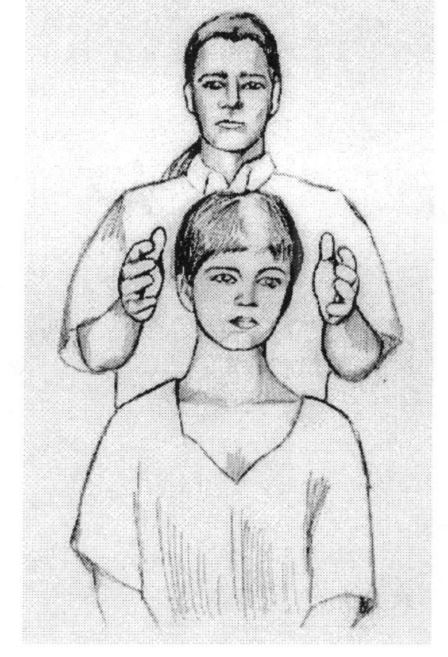

There is only one place on the body where it's best to be cautious; when doing a Closed Loop around the head.

Never place your hands around the head in a position that is ***opposite*** of the polarity for the head.

The head of course has two sides, and like two sides to everything, there is a positive and negative side to the head.

Here's how your head looks magnetically.

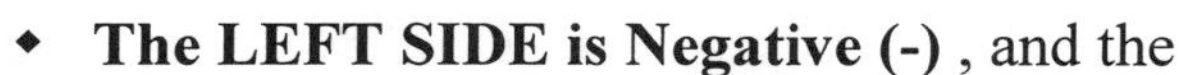

- **The LEFT SIDE is Negative (-)** , and the
- **RIGHT SIDE is Positive (+)**

So, you always use your

- LEFT hand (-) on the LEFT SIDE, and your
- RIGHT Hand (+) on the right side.

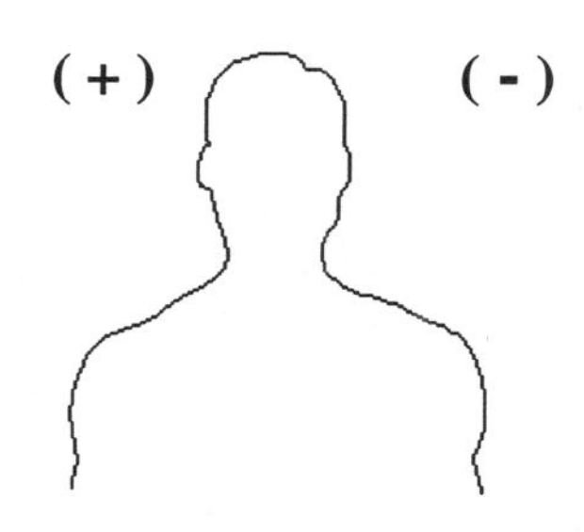


This keeps the polarity the same on both sides of the head just like your hands.

Following this rule will prevent reversing the polarity of the head.

How can you mess this up? By doing the Closed Loop from standing in front of the person.

What can happen if you do? For one thing. . .headaches. That's enough reason alone to hold this positon correctly. If you do happen to get it turned around and you don't notice what's going on until the person you're working with says something like, "My head's starting to hurt." Don't fret. After you say "Ooops," simply change your hand position. That'll turn things around.

The other reason for not reversing the polarity of the head is because all the circuitry that runs the body is centralized in the command center of the brain. The brain must be balanced in order to do its job properly. The Closed Loop helps to balance out irregularities of brain function.

The brain is also where the spinal cord is connected and keeping the balanced flow of positive and negative energy is critical to healthy body functions of brain commands through the spinal column. So, you want to be cautious to not reverse these flows or get them out of balance.

Another reason for proper hand positioning around the head is the proper functioning of the right and left brain hemispheres.

- The left brain (negative) is responsible for the thinking, logical, reasoning abilities we have.
- The right brain (positive) is for the more intuitive, creative, musical, inspirational side of us.

At any one time we may be operating on one side or the other with stronger influence over our decision making processes. The Closed Loop can assist in balancing out these two brain hemispheres in order to be more balanced in our thinking and decision making that utilizes the whole of our abilities.

## Are Some People's Polarity Reversed?

Some people do have their polarity reversed. Reversed polarity can happen at any one place on the body or through out. This means energy tends to move in the opposite direction than most people. Instead of the energy moving upward on the front left side of the body over to the right, it moves from the right upward and down the left. These people are not to be feared. Such people are no different from anyone else and should be treated as equals. For they're just like everyone else, they just happen to have different polarity. (Humorous attempt at social equality for all.) So. . .

## For Reversed Polarity People Show Respect

On rare occasions I've noticed that when a person mentions that when I'm holding the Closed Loop, (regular position) around the head an uncomfortable pressure begins to build up. That's a good clue their polarity is reversed. If that's the case when you do the Closed Loop around the head move around to face him or her and hold the position from the front. If a person's polarity is reversed no concern is needed to make any changes for holding the Drawing In or Putting In position. Generally a whole bodywork-up (following Examples) can assist in correcting reversed polarity problems.

## What About Left Handed People?

Contrary to popular opinion a person who is left handed does not mean the direction of their energy flow is opposite. That just isn't the case. It may be only about one percent of the population is opposite or has reversed polarity. So you can pretty much assume that most persons are negative on the left side and positive on the right side.

To find out if a person is opposite polarity, the easiest way is for them to tell you. They can do this most effectively by telling you how they feel if you hold the Closed Loop around the head from the backside. They will feel a pressure build up. A discomfort. If they report this feeling, there are two ways you can check.

- Reverse your hand position of the Closed Loop by moving in front of the person holding your right hand next to the left side of their head with your left hand on the right side of the head. The pressure will ease if the polarity is reversed. If not, then you can assume it's not the polarity (but something else which you don't know what it is at the moment), and return to the original position.

If you feel that you don't know what to do in the case of someone you suspect to have a reversed polarity of the head simply use Drawing In.

- Hold the Drawing In position over the center of the forehead between the eyes.

(All the other moves and positions of the rest of this therapy will not make any difference.)

## So, To Repeat The Rule For The Head:

- Stand behind the person
- Keep your Left Hand on the left, Right Hand on the right side.

And what else?

- Follow, as always rule #1: Hold till any tingling stops or for no longer than ten minutes.

Now for. . .

## Rule #3

Generally when experimenting with using Putting In it's preferred to restrict your efforts to working with bones, muscle and skin tissue, and only where there is believed to be no evidence of health problems due to virus and bacteria infection. Otherwise, reserve Putting In for use in whole bodywork at the:

- **Heart area and**
- **Solar plexus**

Should you choose to work on the heart area without referring to the whole body work-up the best approach is to use a Closed Loop position by standing on the person's left side. This will help balance out the natural flow of negative and positive energy that runs through the body.

- The front of the body is overall negative(-)
- The back is positive (+)

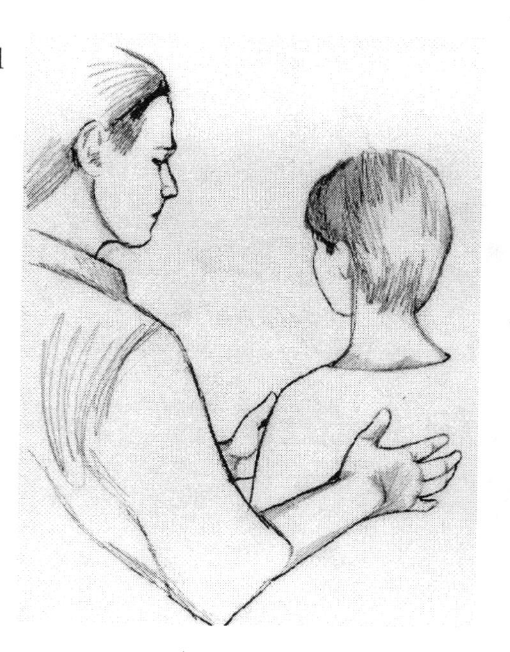

Holding the Closed Loop from the left side position will have your negative (-) left hand in front of the body and the positive (+) right hand on the back of the body.

## Rule #4

- Wash your hands

When able, I suggest washing your hands and arms up to your elbows in cool running water after each time you work with any Wave Therapy hand position with someone.

## Summary Of The Four Rules:

1. Hold any hand position until tingling, or warmth stops, or the ten minute limit is reached.
2. Always stand behind a person for a Closed Loop on the head.
3. Use Putting In for bones, muscle, and skin health problems that are not caused by bacteria or virus infections. Generally reserve for use at the Solar Plexus and the Heart regions.
4. Wash your hands (More on this later.)

Now that you know all the hand positions, and the rules, we can take a look at some examples of how to use the two primary hand positions, the Closed Loop and Drawing In, around the body. Putting

In will be mentioned as an alternate choice in some cases with its uses mentioned in the whole body work-up section.

Onward!

# Examples

## How To Use
## the
## Hand Positions

# EXAMPLES

## *How To Use The Three Hand Positions*

Here are examples of how to use the two most often used hand positions to assist another's body to gain the power needed to recover from common 'household' health problems and illnesses.

### Headache

- Closed Loop or
- Drawing In

Headache that is caused by stress can be greatly relieved through the Closed Loop position. If pain should increase change to the Drawing In position. Drawing In is just as effective especially if two or more people can assist.

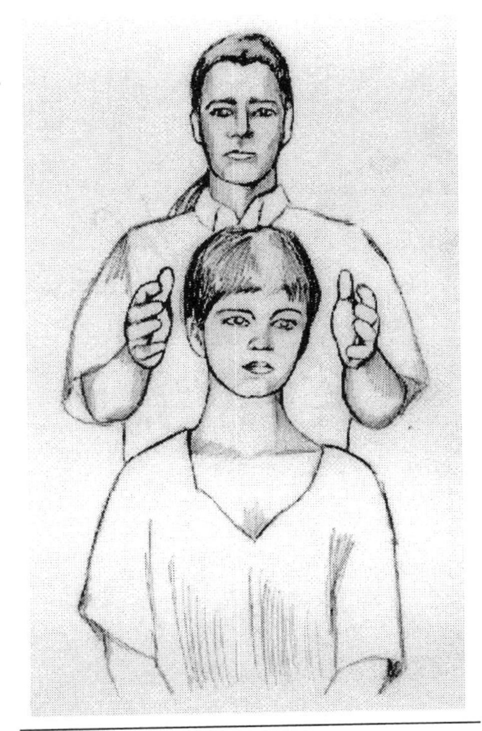

### A Migraine Story

I heard a report from some people at a church meeting where one of the people was suffering from a migraine headache. It had been so bad that she had nearly been incapacitated for a week.

A few people present at the meeting who had learned Wave Therapy in a workshop instructed a couple of others on how to help with Drawing In. So they all gathered around her to see what they could do to help. They all placed their left hands around her head. Within just a few minutes the headache pain had been reduced to a mild ache behind one of her eyes.

After the meeting she was asked how her headache was and with a surprise she announced, "It's completely gone." She had even forgotten about it. A week later there still had been no reoccurrence of the headache.

There is no hard and fast rule which position you have to use. Experiment. The Closed Loop can work fast but can cause a more intense healing crisis then just using Drawing In. If you're in doubt which position to use ask the person you're working with how he or she feels. If the pain or symptoms are increasing from a Closed Loop position, switch to Drawing In.

## Ear Infection

- Drawing In

I've found the best position to use for an ear infection is Drawing In.

The Closed Loop can be too strong for ear infections, and from what I've seen it increases pain with the added positive energy of the right hand in the Closed Loop position. So I use the left hand for negative magnetic energy through Drawing In to calm and soothe and assist the body in overcoming infection.

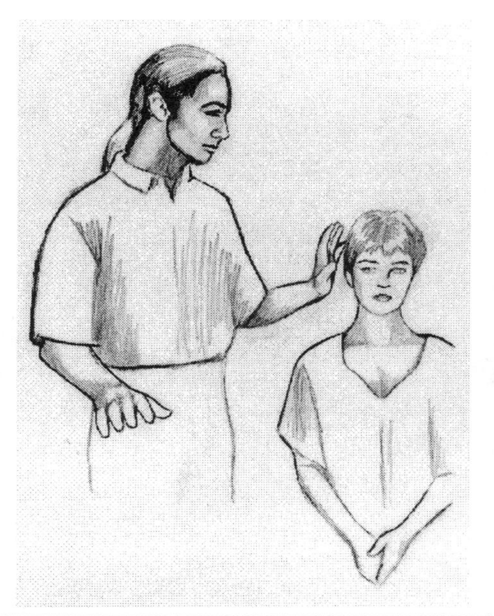

Drawing In is the better choice especially for young children. They are very sensitive to Wave Therapy work and the Closed Loop for any length of time can make them more uncomfortable than necessary. The added positive energy from the Closed Loop can cause a healing crisis.

### Story

I worked with a younger girl of about one year of age when I learned this. I used the Closed Loop for about three minutes but she didn't report feeling much better. In fact she said the pain hadn't lessened at all. That was an unexpected response so I thought there was something I was missing. A couple of hours later my curiosity got the best of me so I called the family to see if there had been a delayed reaction. There was. Her parents reported that on the way home their daughter felt terrible, if not worse. But by the time they had arrived all the painful effects of the ear infection were apparently gone because she went out to play with some of her friends with out a complaint.

## Sinus Congestion

- Drawing In or
- Closed Loop

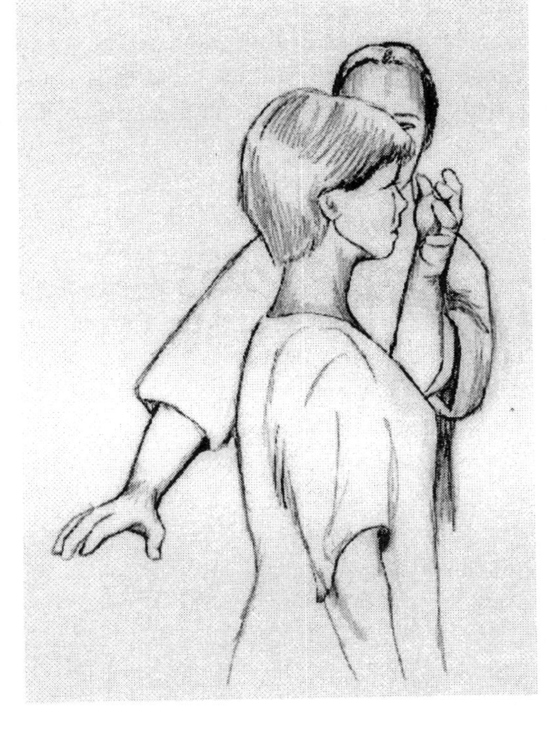

As with any ailment both the Closed Loop and the Drawing In positions can be considered and tried for their individual effects in assisting a person's ability to heal. With sinus problems either position can be used or both. I recommend Drawing In as the position of choice.

- You can hold the Drawing In position with the left hand over the top and the front of the head with the right hand facing the floor. Or. . .

- You can use the Closed Loop position holding your hands around the head with the left hand on the left side of the head and the right hand on the right side of the head, (Standing behind the Receiver). Try either position or both.

## A Sinus Story

Recently I was visiting a friend before going out and having dinner. Also there, was a chaplain friend of his from a local hospital who had been laid up for days with a bad cold. She was undecided whether to go with us because of her stopped up head from the cold. She still had clogged sinuses and couldn't breathe very well. I volunteered to help loosen up her sinuses. I got the regular strange look of "What are you talking about?" I briefly explained the procedure and walked over and stood behind her as she was sitting on a sofa and placed my hands around her head. I held the position for about five minutes while occasionally chatting away with my friend sitting and watching from across the room.

I noticed during the treatment that she was testing her breathing to see how effective this procedure was. So I finally asked her, "Well, are you getting any better?"

"Uh huh. I'm breathing better."

"Good," I said and continued.

I then switched and held my left hand down more in front of her face directly over her nasal area with my right hand facing the floor holding the Drawing In position. I held for about two more minutes until I noticed the increasing look of hunger on my friend's face across the room and decided for now it was time to stop what I was doing and move on. A feeding would do us all good.

So, I stopped and sat down to ask her how she was doing, and she drew in a deep full breath through her nose. A significant change from when I came in. Her head was nearly free of congestion. After a good nose blow, we all left for dinner.

Experiment with both positions. Every person is different in how they respond to Wave Therapy. There can be all kinds of reasons behind what causes the complications. That doesn't have to be your concern here in the practice of Wave Therapy work. But, paying attention does. Listen to both the person you're working with and your instincts. Follow them both, and you will have positive results.

# Tooth Infection

## • Drawing In

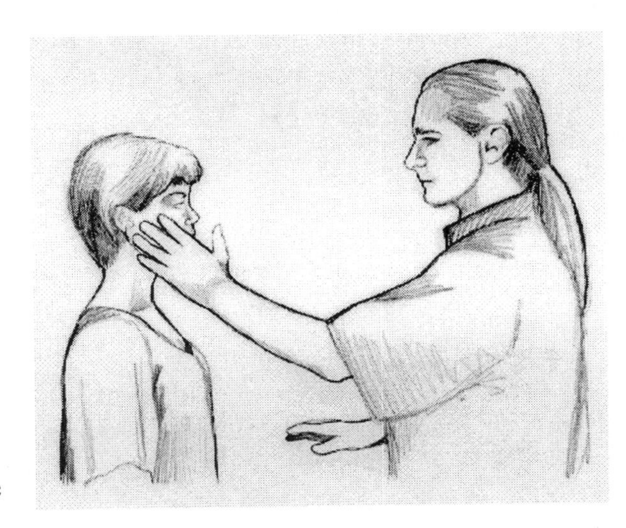

Drawing In is very effective for tooth - aches due to pain from new teeth coming in or from infection. It works surprisingly fast.

- Hold the Drawing In position on the side of the face with the pain. Hold till the pain goes away.

### Tooth Infection Story

Bob, a friend of mine came for a visit one day at work. We had talked about Wave Therapy before but he never had a problem to test to see how it worked. But this day he had one. His lower right gums were infected and he was in terrible pain. He was scheduled to see the dentist again for the problem and was afraid he was going to have to have root canal surgery.

"I don't know about this Wave Therapy stuff", he said,

"But if there is any chance it could work I would like for you to try it out on me" he asked.

Of course I would. So I had him sit in a lobby chair.

I held the position for a few minutes. There was no response from him. He just kept staring straight ahead. So I chatted on about the regular things we chat about which is usually about physics. Bob is a physics teacher and astronomer.

After ten minutes I stopped and asked him how he was feeling.

Calmly he says, "Much better. There's no pain right now."

After some more casual talk he takes off.

A week later Bob comes back to tell me of his news.

"I really didn't believe anything what you've been talking about with this Wave Therapy, but this stuff really works!" When I left the other day I had no more pain and it hasn't come back. I saw the dentist to be sure and there is no infection. I don't have to have surgery. Thanks!"

Then he wanted me to work on other spots on his body that were bothering him.

## Stomach Pain

- Drawing In

This is a fun ailment to work with. . .if you can refer to feeling bad as being fun. But, Wave Therapy can bring such relief by helping to relieve discomfort in the stomach area due to constipation or food poisoning, that it can become a pleasant experience for both you, the Giver and the Receiver. For the Receiver the pain lessens and you the Giver receive the pleasure of helping.

For a general ache or pain in the stomach region first try using the Drawing In position.

- Hold the Drawing In position with the left hand over the stomach area, right hand facing the floor, and hold. Hold until the discomfort goes away or until the ten minute rule is reached.

I have worked with many people where stomach ailments are due to constipation or an impacted colon. In fact over the years I've come to wonder how many illnesses we have may simply be due to the body not being able to eliminate toxins, harmful bacteria and virus because of a congested intestinal track. Should you have problems with constipation or an impacted colon, here is the move using both hands that can help loosen things up. It's a rotating Closed Loop over the abdominal area.

## • Rotating Closed Loop

With the right hand on the lower abdomen area and with the left hand positioned just below the rib cage at the top of the stomach area, begin:

- Rotating your hands in a circular direction, swirling your hands around in a clockwise circular motion.

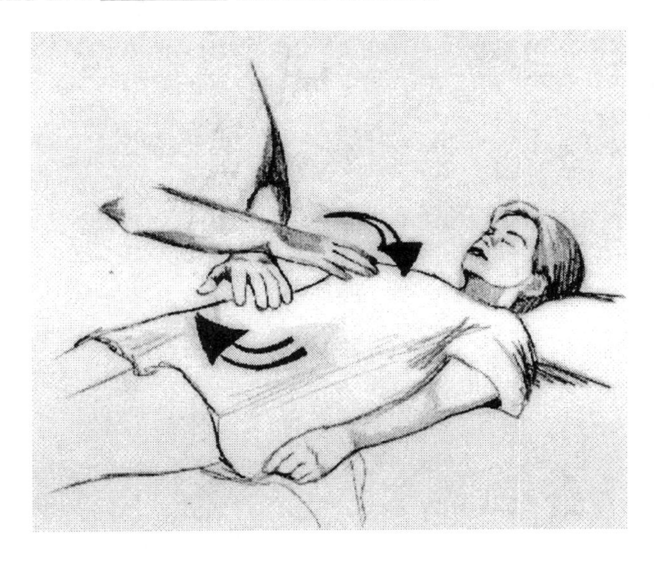

Personally, I get a sense of push and pull going on. I sense a feeling to my movements as if I'm pushing with my right hand and pulling with my left hand. That's what's happening magnetically, and apparently that's what's happening to the material in the colon and intestines.

With practice the Giver will feel the push/pull effect as well as the Receiver. Should you not feel this affect in your hands, I recommend doing this move during a whole body session for the body receives an increase in energy level that will be more present to gain more effectiveness in performing this move.

I've worked this rotating Closed Loop move on many people and the results have always been the same, a wonderful cleansing of the intestines. This move works just as well on adults or babies.

## A Constipation Story

I was asked to work on a child who wasn't a year old yet. When the parents brought him to me I didn't know how serious the problem was. They said he wasn't having bowel movements, and could I help? I told them we'll see.

Well, I came to find out that the little tike had more than a few days without a bowel movement; it was more like a week and he had a huge abdomen to prove it. He was in terrible pain.

I worked on him with the Rotating Closed Loop for about three minutes and they took him home. I was concerned and called the next day to see how he was doing.

The mother was elated. She reported that after they got him home nothing had seemed to happen. By morning, they assumed still nothing had happened for the baby hadn't made a sound through the night. Before the session he would cry in pain, but since the session they hadn't heard a thing. She checked him anyway and to her surprise he had evacuated everything quietly during the night and without pain. And his stomach was flat!

I realize this may not be a pretty story to relate but for some parents, this can be a blessing for those who have babies or young children with severe constipation problems.

You may not get immediate results and have to wait a while, maybe overnight like this couple did before you see results. But you'll get them.

In fact, with all the clients that I work with I do this move on them, because I believe we could all use a little help in this area. So, I forewarn them that they most likely will have a wonderful bowel movement. This conversation keeps things really down to earth during a session.

There are other kinds of stomach ailments besides constipation, viral infections or food poisoning that can be helped. Sometimes there are outside circumstances that can adversely affect our health as with adverse reactions to medications, complications from surgery. Drawing In can help tremendously.

# Nausea

## • Drawing In

Another stomach complication that using Drawing In can help with is for those who go through radiation treatments for cancer. A session for fifteen minutes moving around the whole of the abdomen and pelvic area can successfully reduce or even eliminate nausea that can come from radiation treatments. A thorough whole body work-up would be ideal. For a quick empowerment of the body a ten to fifteen minute Drawing In session can work wonders.

### Radiation Nausea Story

I received a call from someone who had recently had surgery due to testicular cancer. He was now going through follow up treatments with radiation. Since his first treatment, he had been suffering from severe nausea. Enough so he had to stay very near a restroom for he couldn't stop the vomiting. Over the week he had recovered enough so there was only a slight sense of nausea remaining. When he called he was scheduled for another radiation treatment for the following day and was wondering if what I did could help at all to minimize the sickness.

"Let's try and see. We certainly can't lose anything."

We agreed he would come by my place immediately after his treatment and we would try a simple fifteen minute stomach session.

I got carried away as usual and went for thirty minutes with the first session, adding the short version of a whole boy work-up. (See short version in the full body work-up section.)

He left without feeling any sense of nausea. The true test would be in a couple of hours. Because for him that's when the effects of the radiation treatment would settle in.

The treatment was in the afternoon and along toward mid evening my curiosity got the best of me and I called him to see how he was doing.

"Just fine!" he said. "No problems. I feel good."

"Any nausea?" I asked.

"No. After your treatment, it felt like there might be something coming on but it went away and I haven't had any problems. "

"Thanks a lot."
"That's absolutely wonderful!" I said excitedly. It worked!"

I had no idea how well the therapy session would hold against the strength of radiation on his body, but it did. And it did so magnificently. I was excited for him feeling well and also for another victory for the power of such a simple way to manage better health.

For his next scheduled radiation treatment he came by again. Still no nausea. We held to the fifteen minute original plan this time. The first treatment held out for the week. Would the fifteen minute treatment do as good a job? It did. No ill effects occurred.

For my reward I got a nice dinner out of the deal.

For people who undergo treatments for cancer there's a reward for them too in trying Wave Therapy. It can help them deal better with getting over the complications of nausea from cancer treatments. This therapy can do wonders for their health.

## Lump In Breast

- Drawing In

I mention this condition not to promote the idea that Wave Therapy techniques can be a cure-all for cancer, but should you know someone who does develop a lump in the breast you can at least try this work. Wave Therapy is here for you to try in doing your part to participate in some way with your health and recovery, no matter what the health condition. Keep in mind that Wave Therapy is not designed to replace any prescribed medical practice but is to complement and work along side conventional medicine.

## Lump Story

I have a friend I've known for nearly twenty years who called me soon after I had started experimenting with Wave Therapy to see how it could help her after she had discovered a lump in her breast. She had been to the doctor, had x-rays, and it was recommended that she return the following week for more observation and consideration of treatment after a biopsy was done.

She asked me if the work I was doing with energy could do anything for her. I told her I honestly didn't know. I hadn't dealt with this complication yet, but we had nothing to lose in trying. So she came by.

I held the Drawing In position over the area for about ten minutes when the tingling sensation left.

The following day was the scheduled doctor's appointment. The result was that somehow the lump was no longer there. After another x-ray still nothing showed. Twelve x-rays in all were performed in an effort to locate that lump, but it just wasn't there to be found.

She hasn't had to go back for the problem since.

Now bear in mind this could have been something entirely different than a cancer growth. But whatever it was, it was there before a Wave Therapy session and gone afterward. And that was good. There was a health complication, we experimented and tried and now she is free from the growth.

With any health complication that comes up, try what you know how to do, see what happens and go from there. That's participating in your health.

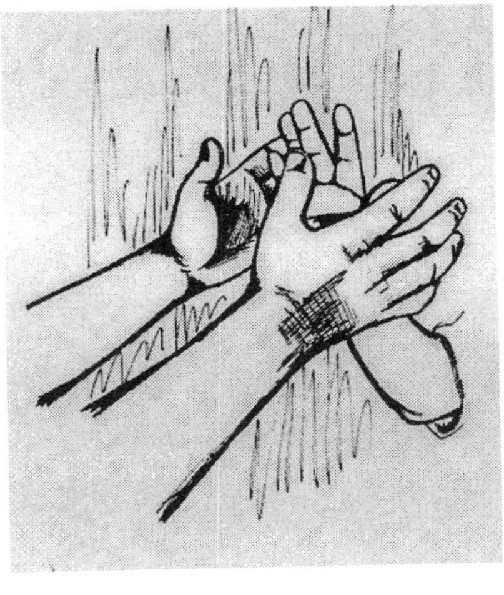

## Arthritis

- Closed Loop

I can't tell you how many people I've worked on with arthritis pain. Anyone who complains of pain in their hands, I immediately stop whatever is going on and work with them. To help relieve arthritis pain in someone's hands is as easy as reaching out to someone. The Closed Loop is the best position. It has worked every time I've tried it on someone from the smallest pain in a finger to chronic aches in knees.

### Finger Arthritis Story

I was browsing in a health book store and found myself chatting away with the clerk behind the check-out desk and conversation causally turned to what I had been doing with Wave Therapy. (He did ask what I do.) After a brief discourse I volunteered to show him the Closed Loop position. So he stuck out his left hand for me to demonstrate. He wanted to feel the tingling thing. I obliged, and he soon felt the sensation growing in his own hands. With that I said,

"See there." An approving tack-on to our conversation that what I was telling him about energy was in fact true. And I left.

About a month later, I was back browsing again and once again found myself wandering back up to the front desk to welcome any chat.

"You remember when you showed me that hand thing?" he asked.

"Oh yeah," I said having forgotten about it.

"That stuff really works. I had a terrible pain in my finger (he showed me his right forefinger) and as soon as you did whatever it is you did on me, the pain left. And hasn't been back. Thanks!"

"You're welcome," I said. Pleased with another convert, I was soon gone after offering a few similar stories of my own.

## Swollen Ankle

- Closed Loop
- Drawing In

Swollen ankles respond well to the Closed Loop. With the push/pull affect of positive and negative energy, fluid build up in any swollen area can be effected. The Closed Loop engages the power of both the positive energy to strengthen weakened muscle tissue and negative energy to assist in calming the effects of pain due to damaged nerves and swelling.

The position to hold for the Closed Loop around a swollen ankle, knee, or elbow is to hold the position that comes naturally to you as you face the person you're working with.

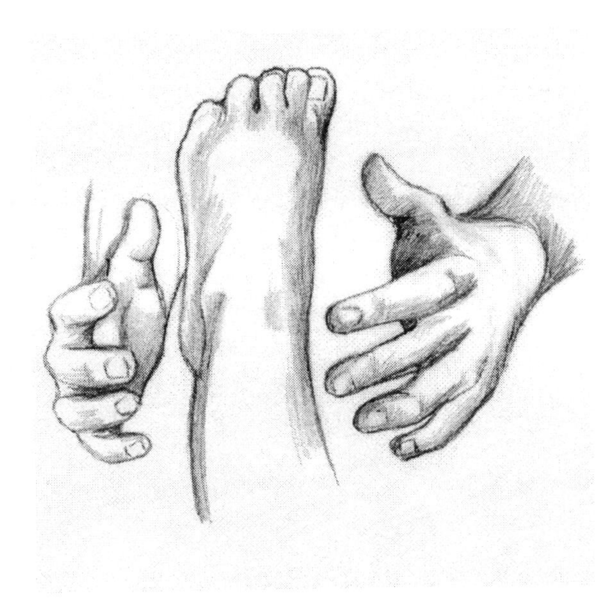

You also can consider doing Drawing In holding your left hand just above or below a swollen site. Drawing In engages the pulling influence of negative energy. Pulling fluid away from a swollen area can help reduce pain and swelling.

### An Ankle Story

I have a story to offer that comes through an experience of my editor. As she was helping me to edit this book, she decided to try out Wave Therapy on a friend of hers who was complaining of a swollen ankle. He reluctantly agreed to let her try. Neither one of them felt any tingling but he had confessed to feeling a little warmth. After she stopped holding the position he said,

"This doesn't work. I didn't feel anything."

But she says when he left he walked away without the limp he had when he came to see her!

Tah dahh!. . .is all I've have to say.

## Burns

### • Drawing In

Drawing In works excellently for relieving pains due to burns. It even helps prevent swelling, infection and fluid from developing around the area if administered immediately after the incident.

### My Burn Story

I've did Drawing In on myself one day after receiving a steam burn from a boiler where a leak had developed in a pipe and burnt my right hand. I caught myself in time to hold my left hand over the area. I could feel the tingling sensation begin and the pain slowly start to diminish. I held the position till the pain was gone which wasn't very long.

The following day where there would usually be swelling and fluid build up there was only a slight pink color to the skin where the burn occurred. Fortunately the burn area was where I could use my left hand for Drawing In. If it had been on my left hand I would have tried to have someone else help me with it.

For similar incidents like for cuts and bruises the Closed Loop works really well.

## Cuts/Bruises

- **Drawing In**
- **Closed Loop**

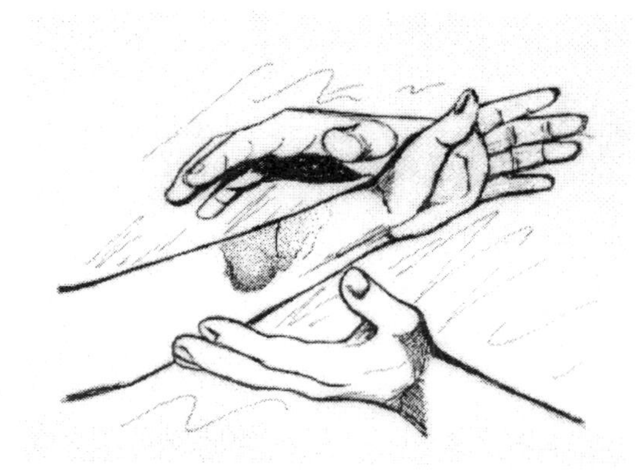

Cuts of course mean pain so Drawing In is best to use to help relieve the pain. The positive energy of the right hand can also help speed healing recovery of skin tissue so the addition of the right hand with the left in the Closed Loop can also be advisable. If pain doesn't diminish from a fresh wound with the power of the both energies of the Closed Loop switch to Drawing In. For a cut or scrap you may notice a stinging sensation when a Wave Therapy position is beginning to do its work to assist the healing process. If you want to help insure against any scar tissue build up continue with daily sessions while the body is working on healing.

## Blood Clots

- Drawing In

Working with blood clots calls for Drawing In. A person may not normally come across this event but should it happen Drawing In is very effective. Drawing In as you now know helps relax and ease tension. It also helps draw in oxygen to an area, which the blood is responsible for in delivering to all parts of the body. The relaxing negative magnetic influence of the power of life will help counter the positive energy effects of the clumping of blood in the body.

I had an experience while working in the hospital where a patient was suffering from a blood clot in the right leg.

### Blood Clot Story

I was working as a hospital chaplain in a Veterans Hospital when once in making my rounds I visited a man who in the course of conversation reported he was scheduled the following day to have surgery for a blood clot in his leg. I was fairly new on staff at the time and hadn't quite worked up the nerve to discuss with the head nurse about Wave Therapy and how it could help patients. My role as chaplain had a standard of being a bit more passive than what additional services I was planning to offer.

So here we were. A man laying in a hospital bed in pain, scheduled for surgery to remove a blood clot. Then there was me with my decision to offer assistance. What to do? Surgery? Or. . . Drawing In?

I considered the options for a few seconds and went for it. Being the Chaplain suggesting prayer was a great way to sort of sneak in Drawing In.

"Say, ..." I said. I have kind of an unusual prayer style to offer that may help you with your leg problem. Would you like to try and see if it works?"

"Sure, why not. It couldn't hurt," he replied.

So I offered a prayer for healing while holding my left hand over his left leg. I continued to hold the position after the prayer and explained the action I was doing was like a prayer and we could go ahead and talk a bit while God was doing his work.

After a few minutes in walks a nurse. She stops at the head of the bed looking at what I'm doing which more than likely was an unusual chaplain position than she had seen before.

"What are you doing?" she asked protectively.

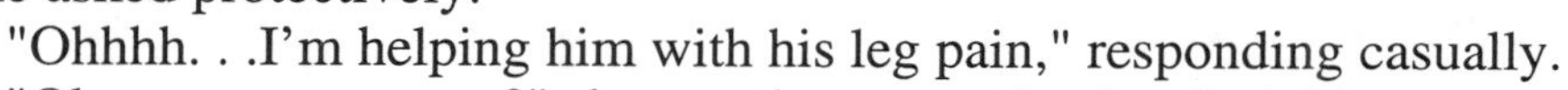

"Ohhhh. . .I'm helping him with his leg pain," responding casually.

"Oh, you are, are you?" she says in a tone, that implied this chaplain is a crazy one.

The nurse moves over to her patient's left side, leans over to him and asks kindly,

"Well. . .how's your pain,?"

I'm still holding the Drawing In position.

The man puts his arms around behind his neck, looks up at the nurse and a wide grin spreads across his face. As lazily as giving her the time of day he answers,

"I don't have any pain."

The nurse straightens up, apparently surprised at his answer. Of course, I crack a slight smile. Not too noticeable. (On the inside I'm yelling. . . Yeeessssss!)

She pats him on the shoulder with a congratulations for feeling so well and leaves the room to look in on her other patients.

We finish up our conversation and I tell him I'll come see how he's doing in a couple of days.

My work schedule had me off for the next four days. When I returned the man was not in his room. Come to find out from the nurse that for some reason the blood clot had dissolved, he was doing fine so they released him without surgery.

## Pneumonia

- Closed Loop

As serious a condition as pneumonia is every medical precaution should be taken under a doctor's supervision. I have to tell you that for me the recovery experiences I have witnessed in working with people who suffer from this health problem have appeared to be nothing short of miraculous.

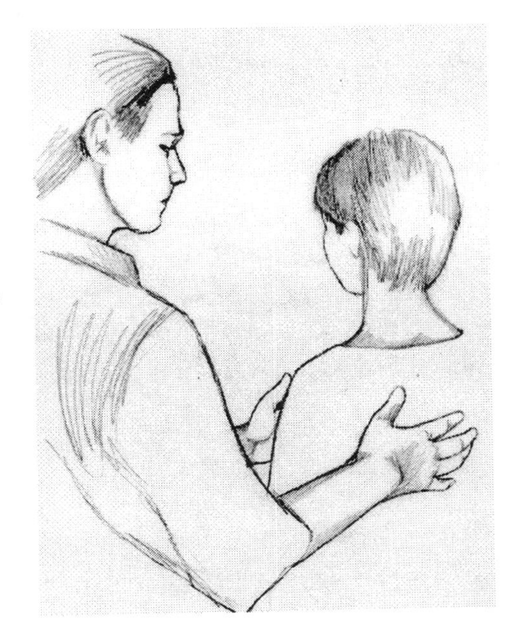

Working Wave Therapy may not work in the same way for everyone for each person and any situation can have different circumstances that may effect the outcome but by all means don't neglect to offer assistance. The Closed Loop is very powerful tool to help someone fight this illness.

### Pneumonia Story

This is another hospital story.

The diagnosis for the patient was not good. The gentleman who I will call Marty was believed to be on his deathbed. Last rites had already been delivered when the family had the nurse call for me. I was on call at the time so another chaplain on the floor had made the initial visit at the doctor's request.

I had visited with Marty on his previous stay in the hospital from a complication with pneumonia. He had his right lung removed several years ago and was on oxygen from emphysema complications.

On our introduction on his last hospital stay I had offered to pray with him using my "unusual prayer method" of holding my hand around his chest. He had liked the idea. (I worked on his feet too. They were hurting) The following day he had recovered so much from the pneumonia that he was soon released from the hospital. Now he was back an apparently in a much worsened condition.

As part of my chaplain duties I would submit written reports of patient visits to the Head Chaplain. Here's the written report of what happened beginning with a call from a nurse.

Nurse: Chaplain Winters, Mr. Atkins has been given Last Rites and the family is requesting your presence.

Me: Last Rites? A Catholic priest came and gave him last rites?

(Knowing Marty was not Catholic I was confused, thinking she was talking about another patient.

Nurse: Yes, Well. . .I'm not sure what's really going on. But the family asked that I call you by request of the patient. They said that you were a friend of the family and that the patient wants you with him.

Me: You say the family specifically asked for me?

Nurse: Yes, they did. It took a while for me to figure out who you were by their description, but they have requested you. (Describing me by my hair.)

Me: OK. I'll be right up.

Nurse: OK. (I get to the hospital ward and there are two women I recognize sitting by the phones in the lobby. The wife of Marty and her mother, who is on the phone.)

Me: Well hello there. Did you call for me?

Wife: Hi Sam! Yes, we did. The doctor said he might go anytime so Marty has been asking for you. He really likes you and wanted you here with him.

Me: What a wonderful thing to say. Of course, I'll see him. What's been happening with him?

(She explains that he had gotten worse and they have to put him on a machine that forces the air in his lungs. It's critical and the machine can only be used for 24 hours. If he doesn't make it through that period with improvement his chances are slim that he won't make it.)

Me: I hear that a priest had been here to see him?

Wife: Yes. Some gentleman came up and gave him Last Rites or something. Marty didn't understand a word of what he was saying but he liked it though. He said he liked the words a lot. Most of it he had no idea of what he was saying. But still liked what he said.

Me: A Catholic priest came up? (I was still confused about the nature of the situation since Catholic priests are not generally called for non-Catholics.

Wife: Well, I guess he was. You know I'm Baptist and Marty is Lutheran. Anyway, Marty says he wants to see you. He really thinks of you as a friend. You know how cantankerous he is and how he jokes with everybody. He has a good time and gets along with you real well.

Me: Then let's go see him.

(We get up and walk to his room. I notice there are three or four people sitting around in the waiting room. Marty's wife tells me about one of the daughters being very religious and a Baptist. We get to Marty's room and it's full of relatives standing around. One man sitting down and what I assumed to be his wife moves over and sits on his lap. Marty is not in the room. I say hi to everyone. and there is group hello returned.)

Me: Where's Marty?

Son: He's in the bathroom.

(I reason that this situation is not to critical if Marty has gotten up to go to the bathroom.)

Me: Well, he must be doing fairly well?

Son: Oh, you know Marty. He's gotta keep moving all the time.

Wife: He quite himself giving everyone a hard time. (Laughs)

(Marty comes out of the bathroom, in a wheelchair and rolls over to the bed.)

Me: There you are!

Marty: (Smiles a toothless grin. His teeth were out.)

Hello. Good to see you. (And makes some joke about the nurse. He gets up out of his chair and removes the oxygen hose to his nose that is attached to the portable wheelchair tank, walks to his bed to pick up the other hose connected to the wall oxygen.)

Turn that thing off for me would you? (The wheelchair tank)

Me: Sure. (I turn off his tank. Then all the people in the room get up and leave, except for his wife. A sudden Exodus!)

Daughter: We're going to go out and get something to drink. Dad's had a lot of excitement tonight and needs to have a little more quiet. He can't stand it that with that mask on because he can't talk.

You know how he is? Gotta makes cracks about everything all the time.

Me: I know he does. He quite a guy.

Daughter: He sure is.

Son: Well, we'll leave you now.

Me: All right.

Me: Marty you seem to be breathing pretty good. What's going on?

Marty: The doctor say's I've got some kind of bacteria in my blood or something. Come over here and pray for me like you did the last time. It helped me out a lot then.

Me: Well, all right. I'll be glad to. I'm glad it helped you out.

Wife: It sure did. He told everybody about it. And how you helped him with his feet to. He's told everybody that for days after you worked on his feet he didn't feel any pain for three days. Then it started to come back.

Me: I can show you sometime how to do it for him. It's real simple. (She nods her head)

(I move to climb under his oxygen hose to sit down next to Marty on the bed.)

Me: Let's have a prayer together.

(Say prayer, while holding my hands on both sides of Marty's body, front and back of his chest in the Closed Loop position. One of the men comes back into the room and stands there to watch. After the prayer I look out into the hall and the hallway is lined with people standing and watching. The whole family must have been there. I counted thirteen people in all.)

Me: Say! You've got one big and loving family there Marty. They're all here to be with you. They must love you a lot.

Marty: Oh, yeah. (Breathing heavily) ( I continue to hold position.)

Wife: He's got six on his side and three on mine. Not counting all their kids.

Me: How are you feeling now Marty? Is this doing anything?

Marty: Uh, huh. The pain's gone.

Me: Good. That's something anyway.

Marty: It sure is.

(I plan to hold the position for about five more minutes while a nurse comes in. Another walks down the hall and looks in and smiles. The whole family still staring in from out in the hall. I motion them all to come in. No one moves.)

Me: Why are they all standing out there for? They can come in.

Wife: Oh, they're just giving him some room to be quiet. With all of them around he has to talk too much. He's getting tired.

Me: Marty, I notice your shoulder is having trouble. Has it been hurting you? (Insert - After practicing a while you can sense where energy is blocked in an area to signify a health problem.)

Marty: Uh, huh.

Wife: That's where he had his surgery. They cut him open all the way down here and across (Draws a circle around her chest)

Me: How's it doing now?

Marty: It feels better.

Me: Is he having some kidney problems too? (I move my hands down and feel the blocked area.)

Wife: Yes. His kidneys have not been working to well.

Me: (Ten minutes pass) I'll stop now so you can get some rest. (Remove my hands and crawl back under the oxygen tubes.)

Marty: OK. Thanks.

Me: You're welcome. I hope that helps you some.

Wife: I'm sure it will. It sure helped him a lot last time.

(The crowd starts to leave and move on down the hall into a waiting room out of sight.)

Me: I'll leave you to rest now and I'll check back in with you tomorrow and see how you're doing.

Marty: All right. Thanks.

(I go to write in the charts, talk with the nurse who thought calling for the last rites was premature that the doctors were possibly making a more serious diagnosis than it was. Then set out to leave and meet the daughter in the hall)

Me: Hello. He seems to be doing pretty well. Where did everybody go?

Daughter: Dad told everybody that when you got here they were to leave the room.

Me: (Surprised) He did?

DU-4: I'm concerned if he's saved. (She was a Baptist)

C-28: You might be surprised at what's really in his heart. That we can't know. But this I do know. He asks me to pray for him. And he prays with me. He must have some connection to God he doesn't let anyone else in on. Sort of a private man about his spirituality. Have you offered to pray with him?

Daughter: Oh no! I guess that's why he asked you up here. He won't talk about it with the rest of the family.

Me: (Now understanding her background I say...) The scriptures say that he who calls upon the name of the Lord shall be saved. And if any man is not against me is for me. He certainly acknowledges God in some way when we pray together.

How about I show you a type of prayer that you can do with your father like I did? It may give you something to start with in bringing you and your father together to talk.

Daughter: Sure!

(I tell her about laying-on-of hands in a non-touch fashion using the Closed Loop.)

(Marty's wife comes up to us from leaving the room)

Wife: How about we walk down stairs together to get a coke?

Me: Sounds good to me!

(As we leave some of the family starts coming out of the waiting room to head back into Marty's room. I figured since I was out of the room now, the coast was clear and they were all free to go back in.)

The next day Marty's conditioned had improved over night.

Once again I was off for the next few days but when I returned Marty had been released from the hospital.

Now for the next health problem affects a lot of people. How to work with. . .

## Shoulder Pain

- Closed Loop

Whatever may be the cause of shoulder pain, and stiffness, the best choice is the Closed Loop since we're dealing with muscle, tendon and bone tissue.

Hold the position for several minutes and have the Receiver test for results of any decrease of pain or stiffness by increased pain-free motion ability. Then continue as needed.

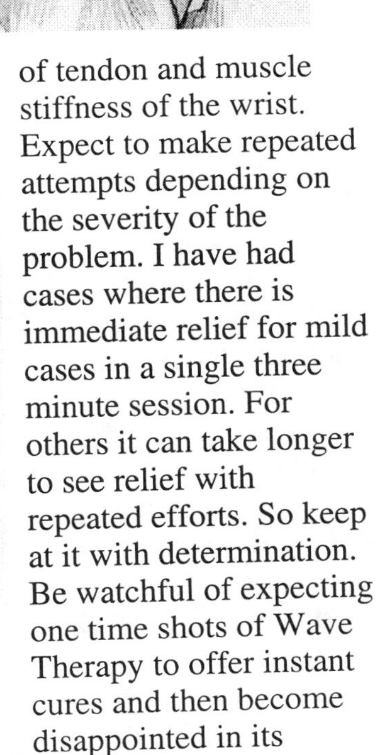

## Carpal Tunnel

- Closed Loop

The Closed Loop is very effective in helping to relieve pain of tendon and muscle stiffness of the wrist. Expect to make repeated attempts depending on the severity of the problem. I have had cases where there is immediate relief for mild cases in a single three minute session. For others it can take longer to see relief with repeated efforts. So keep at it with determination. Be watchful of expecting one time shots of Wave Therapy to offer instant cures and then become disappointed in its

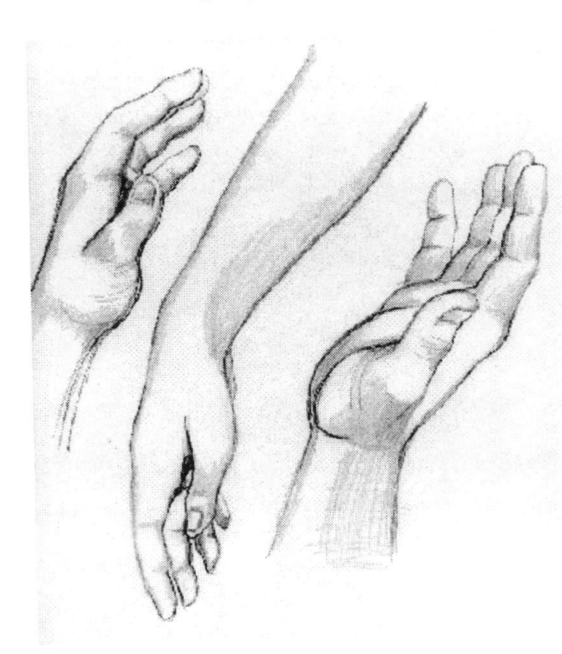

effectiveness when it doesn't happen. It's not the technique that cures. It's always the body that cures itself when given the correct resources it needs to do its job. That goes for any health complication you face. Wave Therapy serves to help stimulate the increase of the body's reserves of the power of life to maintain balance and harmony of energy.

## Carpal Tunnel Story

I spotted a young lady in the lobby of a business who was with a group of friends. She had her right wrist bandaged up in one of those wrist braces to restrict movement. I was fairly certain of what the problem was. I had gotten used to going up to strangers in public and asking about their health condition when I would see obvious indicators like this brace. So I approached her to offer assistance knowing I could help. I asked her about her wrist.

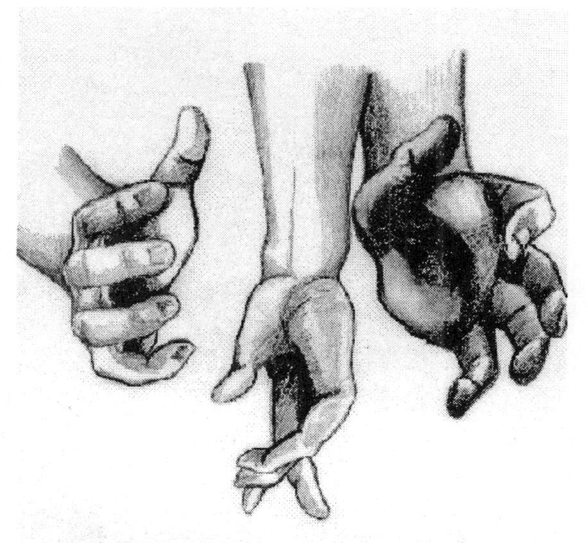

She confirmed she had been having what she believed to be carpal tunnel syndrome. So of course, I followed through with what I intended to do and said I had found a wonderful technique that may help her with her wrist and would she like to try it? I assured her I wouldn't be touching her in any way to cause pain and explained how I would simply hold my hands around her wrist. She agreed to try.

I held the Closed Loop position for a couple of minutes while we chatted about the meaning of the familiar tingling and heat sensations she was experiencing. After about three minutes I asked her how her wrist felt. She started to try and wiggle her wrist a little. Then took her brace off.

"There's no pain when I move it!" and continued to turn her wrist in all different directions to test out her new freedom.

"Thanks!"

"If the pain and stiffness start to come back, just have someone do what I did," I instructed, And off I went.

## Elbow Problems

- Closed Loop

Just as with carpal tunnel, the Closed Loop does wonders for any stiff joint and tendon problem. The cause can be any number of things. With arthritis there may be mineral deposits in the joints. The Closed Loop can help break down those deposits in the joints from the combined efforts of both the positive (+) and negative (-) influences and to help relieve pain in the nerve endings.

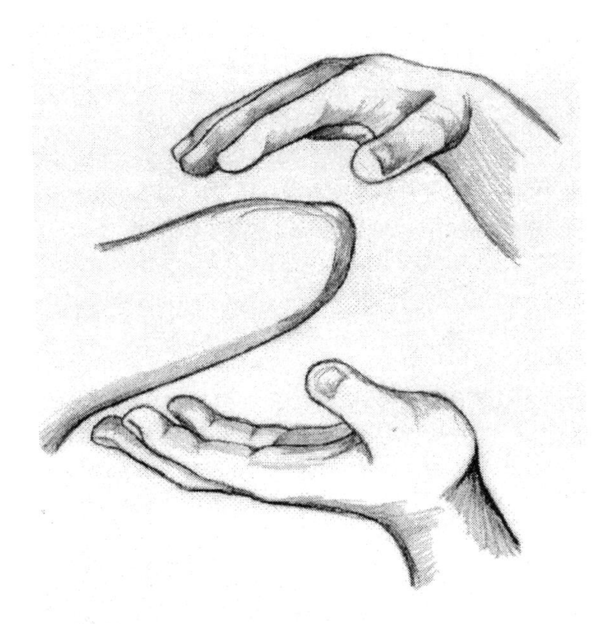

Now to outline for you the final example of this section in how to work with overcoming the symptoms of the common cold and flu.

## Colds and Flu

- Blood Cleanser
- Rotating Closed Loop
- Drawing In
- Closed Loop

Knowing how to work with Wave Therapy to help others overcome the awful and annoying symptoms of colds and flu is worth all your efforts in learning and practicing this information. Amazingly quick results can happen. I've worked with many people to help reduce their healing time from what is usually a week to consistently be almost overnight or even within an hour depending on the severity of the illness.

Ideally a full body work-up (next section) is called for but satisfying results can occur by applying a series of the various hand positions learned in this section. One new position I'm sneaking in here called the Blood Cleanser, is another name I attach to the movement you will learn in the full body work-up section called the Body Scan. (pg. 150)

The Blood Cleanser is an easy move to perform where you simply use the Drawing In position of moving the left hand slowly in a circle around the entire body. I'm bringing this information up here because a full body work-up though extremely beneficial isn't necessarily required in order to assist someone to overcome the cold or flu virus.

## A Cold Story

I received a call one late afternoon from a lady who was experiencing the symptoms of what appeared to be the beginnings of a nasty cold. As with any cold it's never convenient timing and certainly this was the case for her. Judy was scheduled to leave the following morning to visit her grandchildren out of state and she was concerned not only about feeling so bad to be unable to make the trip but if she went anyway how responsible would that be in being around others. Not only for her family but for the people around her on the airplane she was to take to get to her destination.

I volunteered to come right over to see what I could do to help.

I found her stretched out on the couch looking miserable. Her sinuses were stuffed up. Tissues at her side.

I set to work.

I balanced out her field. (Which you will learn in the next section)

Then I started with Drawing In at her left foot and moved my hand slowly up the leg to the top of the head and back down the right side to her right foot. This move applied negative healing energy to help her body fight off harmful virus and bacteria in her blood. (This is the Blood Cleanser move.)

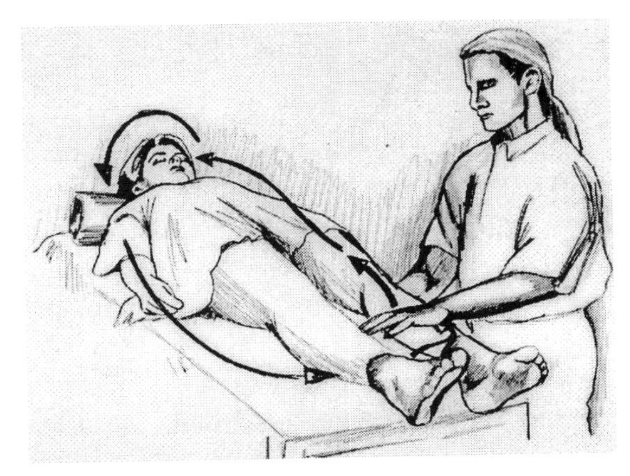

Next I did a Rotating Closed Loop over her stomach. Then I did Drawing In at the front of her head over her sinuses and held for about two minutes. I was done. The rest was up to her.

I left.

The next morning I got a call from Judy for a report. She was preparing to leave for her trip.

"Well, how are you feeling Judy?"

"I can hardly believe how good I feel. After you left I got up and I let loose with a few good sneezes. I thought this meant I was getting worse. Instead I went to bed and had a good night's sleep. This morning I woke up refreshed with not a hint of any cold symptoms. It's like a miracle!"

"That's wonderful!" I said, surprised myself with such a quick recovery.

We chatted a bit more about the event before she had to leave to catch her plane.

## A Flu Story

I had an employee who worked as a desk attendant where I work one day who asked to leave because he was feeling miserable from the flu. He had been vomiting what seemed all the night before, had a fever and wanted to go home. For him to go home meant I would have to replace his presence at the front desk for the remainder of the day. I didn't much care for that idea at the moment for I had other things planned. Considering to help him to get over the flu in this case was for my benefit as well as for his. So my motivation here for his recovery I have to admit, was slightly on the more selfish side.

Considering my attitude about that for a moment I went ahead to venture out and see what I could do to help.

"I can help you get over that flu bug pretty quickly if you like," I suggested, knowing full well he would much rather be going home to bed. He agreed anyway.

I explained briefly what I would do. He had never experienced Wave Therapy before other than a brief demonstration of how to feel the tingling sensations in the hands.

"Come with me," I said" and lead him into my therapy room located in the same building.

"Come over here and sit down," I asserted before he could change his mind.

He sat down on a stool I had parked in a corner.

I began the Blood Cleanser move of slowing moving the left hand in the Drawing In position beginning at the left foot up the leg and left side of the body and back again down the right.

I did the Rotating Closed Loop over his stomach for about five or six turns. Then held a Closed Loop position from the back of his head for a few minutes for the headache and fever. After that I held the Drawing In position over his forehead. The whole process took about five minutes.

Hoping he was feeling much better, I asked him,

"Well how are you feeling now?"

"This is something else. I don't feel feverish any more, my headache is gone and I don't feel nauseated. In fact I feel real hungry all of the sudden."

"Great!" I said, happy for him and for me.

"I'll run out and get you something to eat!" I volunteered.

His strength recovered more after he had something to eat. He felt a little tired the rest of the evening but no more symptoms of the flu remained. I got to go ahead with my plans and he got over being sick, so we both benefited.

## More

There are a host of other areas which you can work with using these hand positions, as with complaints of liver problems or pancreas, feet, knee problems, gall bladder, urinary infections, joints, heart and chest ailments and many others. The examples here are only a few of the common health problems we all come across that you can help others to overcome. Experiment and practice. By using these simple hand positions you can help others by assisting them to receive the power to heal through the simple laws of magnetism that support the power of life that flows through your hands. With the tools of Wave Therapy at your disposal you can do something about helping others in encouraging theirs and your own body to do its job in maintaining positive health.

## Rule Reminder

Remember to pay attention to the rules while working any Wave Therapy hand positions while working to assist someone with their health.

1. Hold position till tingling or warmth sensation stops or for ten minutes which ever comes first.
2. Always hold the Closed Loop position for the head from behind the person.
3. Use Putting In only where there is no evidence of virus or bacteria infection.
4. Wash your hands up to the elbows in cold running water after working with someone. (More on this in the next chapter.)

# Working With Chronic Health Problems

Now that you know all the hand positions and have seen examples on how to apply them for individual health complaints we will now take a look at how to do a whole body Wave Therapy session.

The whole body work-up is extremely beneficial in strengthening overall health in helping a person to overcome a variety of other problems such as chronic fatigue or simple lack of energy, irritable bowel syndrome, guarding against common colds and flu, helping to relieve depression, high blood pressure, diabetes, chronic pain plus any variety of problems due to compromise of the glands of your body that regulate health involving the endocrine system.

A whole body Wave Therapy session can take about one hour to do. There are only two additional hand movements to learn from what you already know.

So, let's be on our way!

# Wave Therapy

## Whole Body Work-Up

# WAVE THERAPY

## *Whole Body Work-Up*

Welcome to the whole body work-up section.

Working the whole body is as simple as using the positions between the Closed Loop and Drawing In, plus the variation of Drawing In, called Putting In. Doesn't sound too hard, does it? It's not.

There are two main benefits of the whole body work-up.

- Relief of excess stress that settles into the body which can develop into health problems through blocks and leaks to the energy of the power of life the body uses to maintain health.
- Increase the flow and balance of energy through out the body for health maintenance. A great way to complement conventional medicine.

### Review

In the last chapter you learned how to use two of the most needed types of hand positions, the Closed Loop and Drawing In. Plus you learned the third hand position, Putting In, all which can help assist a person's body to gain new energy, vitality, and strength to heal itself. These hand positions help a person to gain strength through the:

- Building effects of positive (+) magnetic energy or the
- Calming, soothing effects of the negative (-) energy of the power of life.

### Benefits of Relaxation

Renewing strength to heal and maintaining of health can be gained through relaxation which is promoted through the negative magnetic influence of the power of life to relieve the stress of too much positive energy maintained in the body. Stress is positive in nature and is good. Too much stress means continued over excitement and use of the body resources of healing energy. I'm not going to preach (at least here!) about the value of performing relaxation exercises to get rid of excess stress in life. But, will mention something I've noticed that occurs in nearly every whole body session I've given. There's a noticeable effect of people becoming relaxed. . .quite relaxed actually.

## Stress

It has become more recognized in notable scientific circles how around 80-90% of our diseases come from too much unresolved stress in our lives. You'll find that when you do a whole body session or even work on just a few areas of someone's body for any length of time he or she will usually end up with a nice relaxed, calmed, sensation.

The relaxation response[5] realized from working Wave Therapy with someone is one of the most beneficial side effects you can expect from treatments. So with that in mind it's time to learn the whole body treatment course so you can put somebody out!

## What To Expect

Some of the benefits of working with whole body sessions are in helping to assist with more complicated health problems. These are problems that require more energy attention than can be helped with working with more isolated cases such as described in the last section as knee pain, headaches, toothaches, cuts, bruises, broken bones, minor infections and so on where the source of the physical problem can be directly identified. The whole body work-up helps to release unwanted stress on the body that block or cause leaks to energy that can lead to disease. It can help with problems of more chronic pain such as Fibromyalgia, repeated headaches, blood sugar complications

[5] The Relaxation Response, Herbert Benson, William Marrow & Co., New York, NY

as diabetes, low or high blood pressure, help with symptoms of immune disorders such as colds, flu, and AIDS, with multiple sclerosis, chronic fatigue, Epstein Bar, depression, skin disorders, scar tissue, yeast infection, memory problems, multiple personality disorders; any health problem that cannot be more readily identified because it involves deeper issues than say. . . of a swollen ankle from tripping down some steps.

These disorders are all problems that I have worked with where there has been significant improvement of the condition. This is not to say that Wave Therapy is a cure-all for these health problems but it does assist in significantly lessening complications and in many cases outright relieves the person from all symptoms. The results will differ for everybody depending on the person receiving, how many sessions are given and the ability of the Giver to allow for flow of energy.

## Story

A lady came to see my who I will call Sally. She wanted to experiment with Wave Therapy to see how it might be able to help her. She reported that she was tired all the time. So I set out to do a whole body session to see what it could do to "soup her up" as I call it.

Towards the end of the session I did a body scan (which you will learn how to do) and landed on her right side around the rib cage where her pancreas was. There was another spot near the center of her body just below the rib cage where her liver was. There was a lot of tingling in my hands going on in these two places so I held the position for a while. (Drawing In)

When the session was over and Sally set up her face looked bright. There was color in her checks and she looked ten years younger. Feeling good, she left and scheduled another session for the following week.

The next week she reported that she had so much energy from the last session she was up for nearly three days. Her energy and attitude had changed so much that her family wanted to know what was going on. She then tells me she had an incurable disease called Hemochromatosis, a liver disorder that produces too much iron. The condition called for having a pint of blood drawn nearly weekly to keep her iron levels down. This kept her anemic. What's worse the condition had developed into diabetes and also affecting her heart. She had high blood pressure as well.

What a shocker for me! I thought she was just tired.

We did another session. Again she looked bright and was feeling good. All together, we had three sessions together.

To shorten this tale, a year later, Sally had only one pint of blood removed over that next year instead of once a week. Her diabetes was gone, her blood pressure leveled out and to top it off she had lost twenty pounds of fat. She was a new person.

These results were fantastic. And not the results of long time experience in doing Wave Therapy. Sally was the first person I had ever done a whole body session with.

### You Can Do It Too

I will walk you through how to do a whole body work-up. It's not required that you have knowledge of how the body works or how and why disease develops to effectively help someone. The body will do what it can do when it has the resources of energy to do its job. A whole-body work-up will help assist a person to increase and balance out the flow of energy the body can use to naturally fight and maintain the defenses it needs to overcome disease.

So let's get on with it!

# WHOLE BODY WORK-UP

### The Long Version

First we'll go over the long version which usually takes about one hour. Then I'll show you the short version you can do in approximately fifteen to twenty minutes.

For the whole body session, the three hand positions described in that last section will be used plus the addition of two other movements which are both motion variations of the Closed Loop. In fact, if you consider all of the movements, you'll notice they're all variations of the Closed Loop position.

To repeat, here are the names of the five hand styles:

1. **Closed Loop**
2. **Drawing In**
3. **Putting In**
4. **The Body Sweep**
5. **Polarity Balancing**

There are six steps to complete a whole body work-up. The first two steps will introduce you to the Body Sweep and Polarity Balancing. The rest involve various uses of the Closed Loop, Drawing In and Putting In to complete the whole body work-up.

# THE TWO ACTION MOVEMENTS

## Step 1

### The Body Sweep

The body sweep may just be a tad excessive to do in public view as you will see.

This is generally the first movement used in an overall session. This movement's is like sweeping a floor with a broom to clean up the dirt. In this case you are picking up "dirt" that's in a person's energy field and tossing it away. Your hands work like a dust pan. Only here, you grab the dirt and toss it. It's not only an odd sight to see someone do this but just as odd to do it!

I still feel a bit peculiar doing this movement because in doing it, it appears to be outrageous. But the benefits to the person receiving this work can be wonderfully refreshing and should be done every time you work with someone. I will refer to the person receiving the treatment as the *Receiver*. The person giving the treatment is the *Giver*.

Oh. . .a warning for the practitioner of the Body Sweep. If you are out of shape, expect that your legs are going to get sore. This move is quite the exercise for the one performing it. Up and down, up and down. . .

Here's how you do it:

## Preparation

- Have the person you're working with stand up and face you.

I prefer the Receiver to be standing because the Giver can work around the body more easily. The Receiver can also be sitting or lying down. In the laying down position you will work with what you can work with from the front of the body.

For the Body Sweep you will be working with:

### The Twelve Lines Of Force

- Divide the body up into twelve imaginary lines to work with.

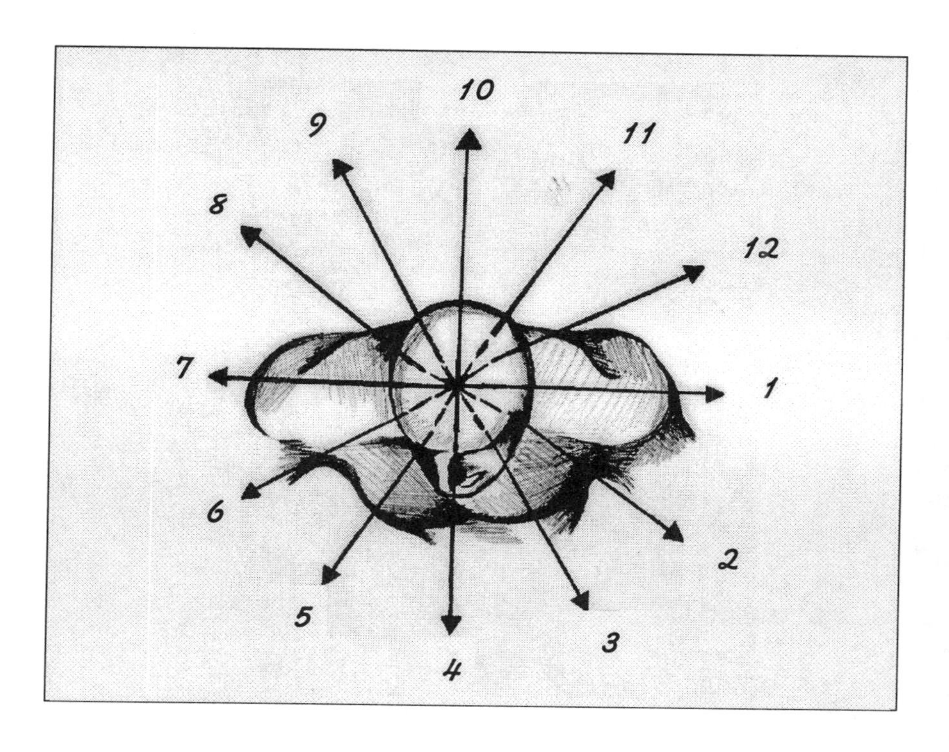

You're going to work with these twelve lines of force. The number twelve has no specific importance to know here only that when you space these imaginary lines about two-three inches apart, the whole body will be surrounded evenly to complete a whole body cleansing of the Receiver's energy field.

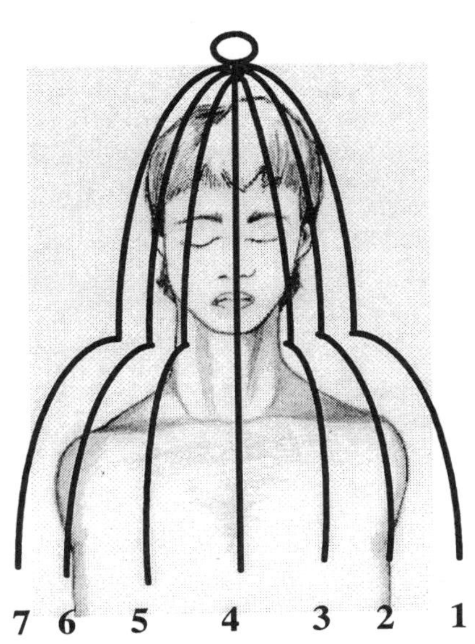


Now for the next step:

- Imagine the Receiver is standing inside a round bird cage with wires all around him/her. These "wires" are like the invisible lines of the magnetic lines of force that are positioned around the body.

The Giver will be making a series of passes around the body by moving from one line of force to the next by sweeping your hands from the top of the head down to the feet along the twelve lines of force.

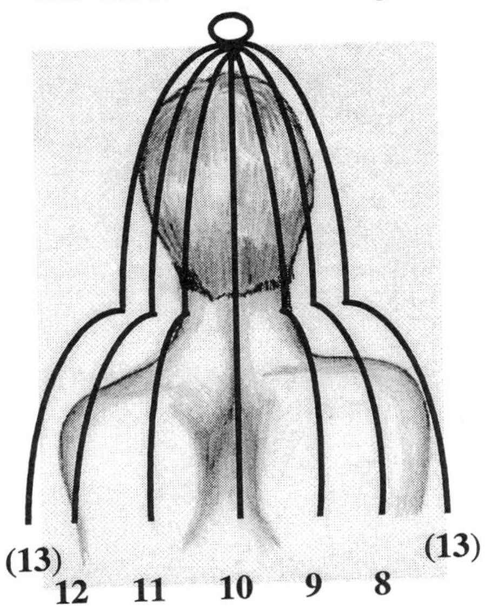


Repeat all the sweeps until you have moved all around the body and return back to your starting position of facing the Receiver. You will find the final sweep will be count number thirteen for the final sweep of repeating the shoulders.

Repeat this series of moves for two full rotations.

## To Do The Body Sweep:

1. Begin with facing the Receiver.
2. Hold your hands above the top of the head without touching. Palms facing downward.
3. Cup your hands slightly and turn them so the palms face slightly outward from each other away from the Receiver's body.
4. Staying close to the body, about one inch, move your hands down the opposite sides of the body, down the sides of the neck along the shoulders and down toward the feet.
5. At the feet, close your hands together as if you have collected something and toss that "something" away to the sides by opening up your hands and flicking your fingers with a snap. If you have trouble bending down towards the feet you could try getting on your knees. (See next page for example.)

That is sweep #1.

- For the second sweep place your hands at the top of the head again and turn them in a clockwise rotation of about one inch to sweep down the second line, for sweep #2. (Your right hand will be on line #2, your left hand on line #8.)

Your right hand will sweep down in front of the Receiver's left shoulder, and your left hand sweeps down backside of their right shoulder.

- Repeat for the third line.

After sweep number three, you will now be ready for the fourth line which will be at the center of the body.

- You should now be standing on the Receiver's right side. The next sweep will be down the center line of the body which is line # 4. (On the back it will be the same as line #10.) Your right hand will pass down the front center of the body and your left hand will pass down the spine on the back side of the body.
- Repeat down each line, for line five and six.

- Line number **SEVEN** is a repeat of the shoulders, from the back position.
- Sweep line eight and nine.
- Line **TEN** will be a repeat of the mid-line. Your Left hand will sweep down the front of the body and your right hand down the back.
- Sweep line eleven and twelve.
- The final sweep will be a repeat of the shoulders again to make the **Thirteenth** pass. You'll be back facing the Receiver again.
- Repeat the whole process again, to perform two sets of sweeps.

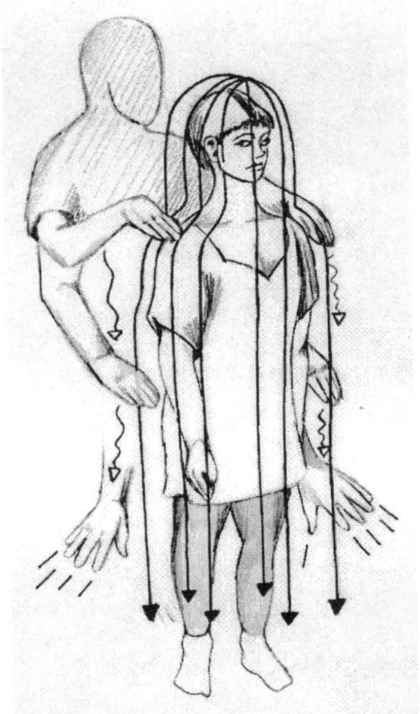

## Simple way to say it

It's may seem difficult in the reading of how to do it but once you start it's quite simple.

1. Just start at the shoulders, facing the Receiver, sweep down both sides and count one.
2. Make a two to three inch clockwise turn and do another sweep.
3. Keep doing the same thing until you have circled the whole body.

That is the Body Sweep.

### Flicking Bad Energy

Don't flick on anybody. This may sound strange, but what you're doing is scooping off debris from around the person's energy field. Remember the magnet? We attract and hold things to ourselves.

Unwillingly sometimes, but we do. The Body Sweep helps remove debris that affects the body's energy field. If someone else is in the room (which I don't recommend, at least not in your line of fire) and you flick in her direction her personal magnetism may attract and hold the debris and affect her.

Many are concerned that flicking debris or "bad energy" on someone can result in the flickee picking up the energy of the problem of the other person and get sick themselves. While this may be true, what also is true is how strong a person's immune system is in overcoming disease. Personally, I have come to find out that a person's positive attitude is stronger than any energy.

## Energy Follows Thought

- Thought moves energy.
- Energy follows thought.

It follows that if you think you're going to get sick, expect it; then get ready, your chances are strong. The opposite holds true as well. So don't be overly concerned about "picking up" someone else's bad energy to get sick. If you find you're a sensitive person to energy and feel like you are picking up stuff you don't want, know that you are just as capable of de-picking it as well.

During any Wave Therapy procedure, it's always a good attitude to hold that as a Giver of energy in Wave Therapy practice you are allowing the energy of the power of life to flow through you to the Receiver. You are not the source of the power of life. Having such an attitude is helpful in your not carrying the weight of being personally responsible for another person's well being. You may be partners in the giving and receiving process of energy movement but you're certainly not their God. Let the power of life flow through you. Should there be any "bad energy" sensed to be flowing into you from the Receiver, let it flow through you as well.

A good physical way to allow this flow to happen is to:

- Hold the Drawing In position with both arms out to your sides. Let fresh energy flow through you from your left hand to the right and out again.

With practice you will get the hang of it.

## Wash Your Hands

In the meantime if you feel weak in this area, a sensible precaution that helps to remove any sense of negative or bad energy moving through you during any of Wave Therapy practices is to wash your hands and forearms in cold running water thoroughly after each session. Wash your hands during a session if you feel the need. Sometimes a Giver's hands may feel like they're loaded down or have a full weighty feeling while working with someone.

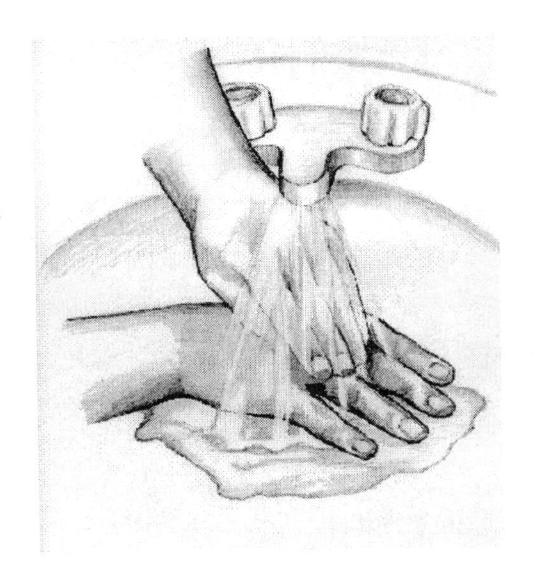

Once while working with a man in a hospital, an onlooker present, who could physically see the working of energy around the body, commented that he could see a dark dense cloud forming around both of my hands. I could feel what he was talking about so I flicked my hands several times towards the floor to shake it off. The hands cleared and the feeling left. (He jumped!)

To help get rid of this kind of sensation flip your hands at the wrist several times till the sensation goes away. Or, you can wash your hands. Keeping a bowl of water handy can be a good idea for such times.

Now, on to the next step for the whole body work-up.

# Step 2

## Polarity Balancing

Polarity Balancing is another motion variation of the Closed Loop.

This move helps to balance and even out the magnetic lines of force of negative (-) and positive (+) influence within and around the body.

## Preparation

Polarity Balancing can have profound effects on people both emotionally and physically; especially the first time they experience it. I suggest you do Polarity Balancing while the person you're working with is at least sitting down. I prefer the person lie down. It's much more relaxing. And it's easier for both of you. A massage table is ideal. It's a good idea too, to add a comfortable pillow under the legs behind the knees. It's a way to help better support the back. Adding a small rolled-up towel under the neck will help support the Receiver's body to be in a more aligned position to allow for better flow of energy through out the body.

Some people I work with go to sleep before I can finish. That's all right. It can be a very healing sleep.

## How To Do It - The Wave

To get the idea of how to work this movement there is a familiar action almost all have us done at one time or another in our lives that looks exactly like it. Have you ever been in a crowd, say at a basketball game, sitting in the bleachers, and you're waiting for friends to show up? Then you see them come into the auditorium. You see them, but they don't see you. What do you do to get their attention? You jump to your feet yelling their names while waving your hands in front of you over your head. First, one arm waves to the left, the other to the right. Maybe you even cross them over each other with the right in front one time, the left the next time, just for added effect.

This waving action is similar to the movement used in balancing a person's energy field.

1. With the Receiver lying down, face him or her.
2. Hold your arms up level in front of you, with palms facing outward over the Receiver's body, beginning with your hands above the top of the head.

3. With the right hand on bottom and the left hand on top cross your hands at the wrist just like the wave example. When you have passed your hands completely over the Receiver's body to the sides, then stop.
4. Next, move your hands down the body about the distance of one hand length to be in position for the next wave.
5. Then repeat the process crossing the right hand under the left, waving your hands over the front of the body.
6. Do this one hand length after another till your reach the feet.

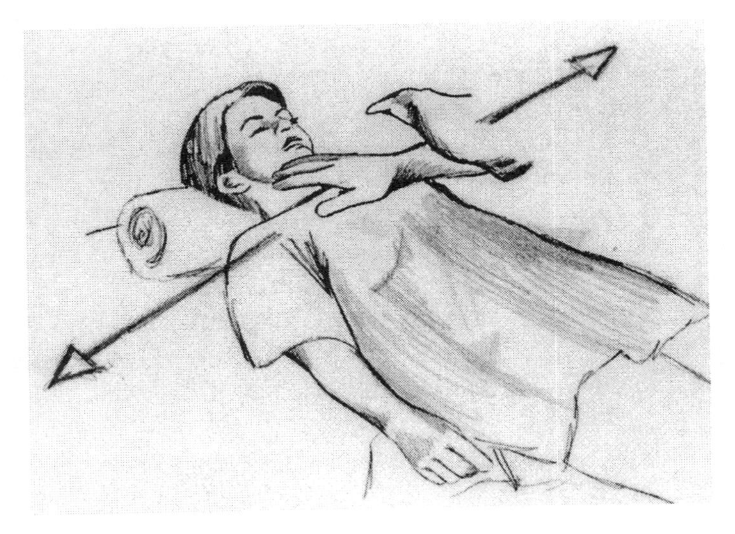

- Repeat the process one more time.

After you have completed the next full body pass, you will have completed two complete body balancing movements with your right hand under the left hand.

Now for a change.

Repeat the same moves down the body two more times but this time you will do it with your:

- LEFT hand facing the person with the RIGHT hand on top. Move down from the head to the feet just like before.

When you've completed these two additional Polarity Balancing moves you will have performed **four** waves over the body. You'll be done.

That is Polarity Balancing.

## How It Works

As we have discovered, everyone has the magnetic influence of positive and negative poles just like the earth has in balancing and holding all things together. These waves of energy are always in motion expanding in and out and sometimes they get moved around and mixed up in and around the body. This mix-up can happen for any number of reasons: environmental influences as disturbing electrical lines in buildings, even power lines, body jolts as from a car wreck, strong emotional surges, and various means we haven't discovered yet. Polarity Balancing helps to move the lines of force back into a more favorable position so the positive and negative energy of the power of life can flow more evenly. Sometimes with just the Polarity Balancing move profound changes can happen within the body and mind simply by bringing order out of chaos.

Here's another way to assist in balancing someone's polarity.

## The Family Version

Here's away the whole family can get together to balance one another. (I use this version too while working with people one on one by moving around to each position.) For group participation it takes six people. Only one hand position is needed; the Closed Loop.

## Preparation:

Have the Receiver lie down in the same manner as described in Polarity Balancing.
While the Receiver is lying down:

1. Have one Giver stand at the head of the one receiving and hold the Closed Loop position.

2. Have the second Giver stand at the Receiver's feet and hold the Closed Loop with the Left Hand facing the bottom of the Receiver's right foot. The Giver's right hand on the Receiver's left foot.
3. The third Giver stands on the Receiver's left side. The Giver's right hand is at the Receiver's left shoulder and the Giver's left hand at the Receiver's right hip.
4. The fourth Giver holds the same position on the other side of the Receiver. With the Giver's left hand palm facing toward the Receiver's right shoulder, the right hand across the Receiver's body, facing the left hip.
5. The fifth Giver stands on one side again, say the right of the Receiver, and holds their left palm facing the Giver's right palm and their right hand palm facing downward over the Receiver's left ankle.
6. The sixth does the same again as the fifth on the opposite side with their left palm facing downward over the Receiver's right ankle and their right palm facing the Receiver's left palm.
7. All Givers hold their positions from three to ten minutes.

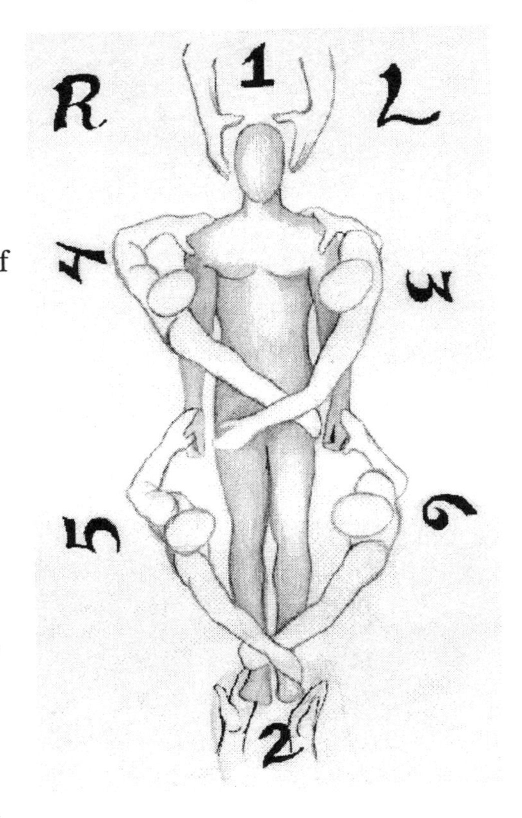


Be sure to watch for anyone touching each other's arm's in the crossing. Keep them apart. The idea is to keep the energy flow moving through all of the Closed Loops without interruption.

You will notice when you work with group polarity balancing not only is there a close sense of community expression of love experienced but the person receiving will also receive great physical and emotional benefits from this work.

When done you can switch and let someone else be the Receiver.

You can do this on your own when working one-on-one together with someone. Simply hold each position starting with the head and work your way through them. I've found holding one to two minutes is usually enough. Watch for the tingling sensations to go down or pressure build up as well to give you a clue when enough is enough. Another good clue to know when to stop, once you get sensitive to the flow of energy, is to feel the sensations in your hands. If one or the other feels more "active" with energy than the other, keep holding the position until they both feel even.

People who I do this move with report a great stretching feeling when working with the diagonal lines across the body.

There!

You've learned how to do the two new hand movements to do a whole body work-up. The two movements of the Body Sweep and Polarity Balancing are the first two steps of completing a whole body work-up. Now we'll go over the variations of the Closed Loop, Drawing In and Putting In to complete a full session.

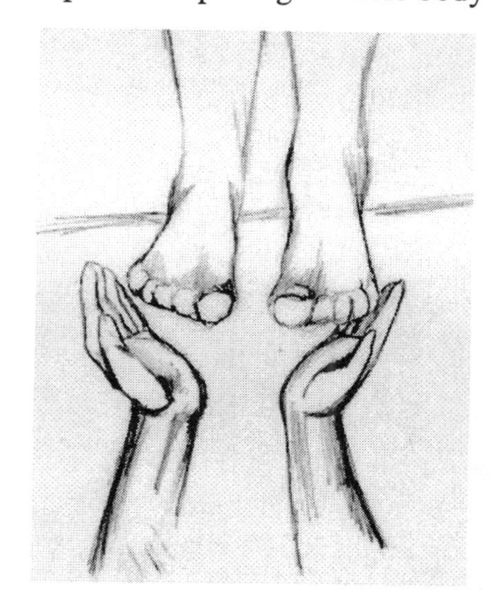

## Step 3

### Grounding

The Closed Loop position held at the base of the feet helps to stimulate the flow of energy in a circular loop through out the body.

It also helps to balance the polarity of the body.

- Hold the Closed Loop at the base of the feet.

You may feel energy stronger in one hand or the other. Hold the position with the intent of waiting until the sense of balance and free flow of energy is felt between your hands. If you don't think you're sensitive enough at any time to feel the differences, holding the position for two to three minutes is plenty of time.

On rare occasions the Receiver may feel uncomfortable with this position indicating his or her polarity is imbalanced or reversed. If this is the case move to the head and hold a Closed Loop.

### Brain Balancer

The Closed Loop at the head also helps to balance out the flow of energy through out the body. It assists in balancing the left and right hemispheres of brain function. The head is a very strong point of magnetic influence that governs all body functions and if the polarity is reversed causing energy to flow in the opposite direction. The Closed Loop can help reverse the flow. Coupled with grounding and Polarity Balancing a reversed polarity problem tends to correct itself. However, I've noticed that with time, the trend is the polarity will reverse itself again calling for another whole body session.

The next step will be using Drawing In to work the Center Magnet. Center Magnet you say? Yes, I did. There's something else to learn. It's time now for a little more news about the body and how energy flows to manage your health.

## *The Center Magnet*

### The Center Magnet

The body is made up of four magnetic pathways. Not something you have to know, but helpful in working whole body sessions to understand how energy flows through the body. All four look like those horseshoe magnets you seen. All four pathways work together to cover the whole body.

1. The first magnet pathway is made up of your legs. Energy flows in a circle up from the left foot to the hips touching the pelvis area and lower intestines and down the right leg to the right foot, and back again. (Viewing this magnet from the back the energy flows in the opposite direction)
2. The second magnet is made up of your arms. The magnetic flows of the power of life moves from the left hand around the shoulders through the throat and heart region and out the right hand.
3. The third magnet is around the head and (for most people) moves from the left side of the head to the right.
4. The fourth magnet moves up the center of the body, beginning in the area just below the genital area and moves upward to the top of the head joining together the other three magnet energy pathways. The Center magnet represents the negative quality for the front side of the body and the opposite positive quality for the backside of the body.

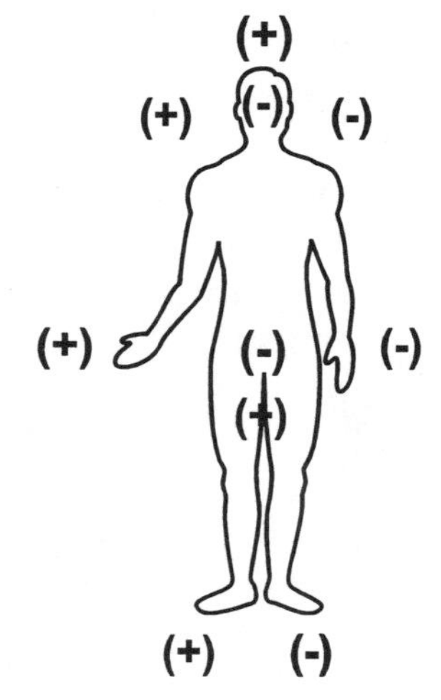


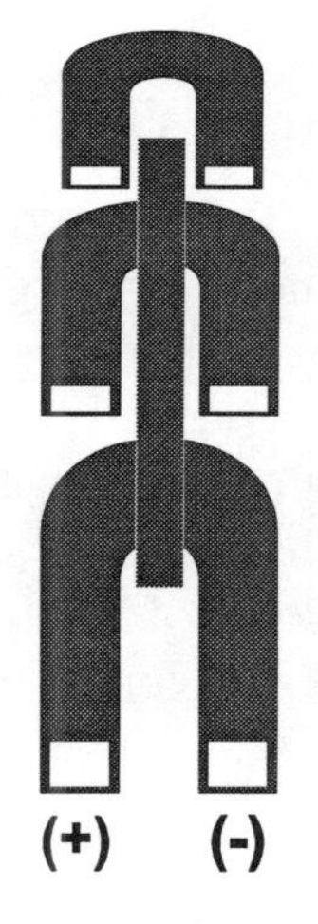


Now to move on to the next movement that will effect all the glands, organs, muscular, skeletal and nervous systems of the body. It's a move that breaks down the Center Magnet in order to work with the individual areas the center magnet affects.

## Step Four

## The Seven Power Centers

This movement will work through seven major areas of energy "pools" in our body. Even though you will work each area separately each one is connected to one another as a working whole.

The center magnet of the body has seven areas I call Power Centers where energy flow moves in and out of us that governs our health.

These seven areas begin at the feet and end at the head. (Or from the head to the feet depending on which direction you wish to begin with.) To work with these seven areas you will primarily use two hand positions, Drawing In and Putting In.

To know how long to hold each position refer to rule #1:

- Hold each position for up to 10 minutes, or
- When the sensation of tingling or warmth stops, which ever comes first.

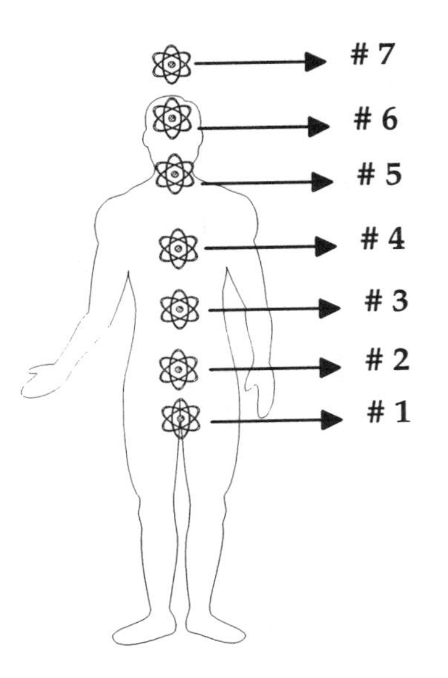


### Preparation

Preferably the Receiver should be lying down for easy access to all the centers. Normally the Receiver will already be laying down from experiencing Polarity Balancing. If the lying down position is not an option then you can also work the centers while sitting in a chair.

You can also work the centers from the back side of the body. All the center positions on the back will be directly opposite the location of the centers on the front side of the body. To work with someone in a chair the Receiver can lean forward for you to position your hand near the body if there is a back to the chair or you can work right through the back of the chair. The material in a chair is no obstacle to the flow of the power of life that moves in and out of us anymore than your clothes are. If that were the case we all would have to run around naked. Wouldn't that make for a crazy world!

For now we will just focus on working with the front of the body.

## Where To Start

You can choose which end of the body to begin working with the Power Centers which ever end of the body you prefer, either at:

- **Power Center #7 at the head, or**
- **Power Center #1 at the feet, and**
- **Work your way through the stops.**

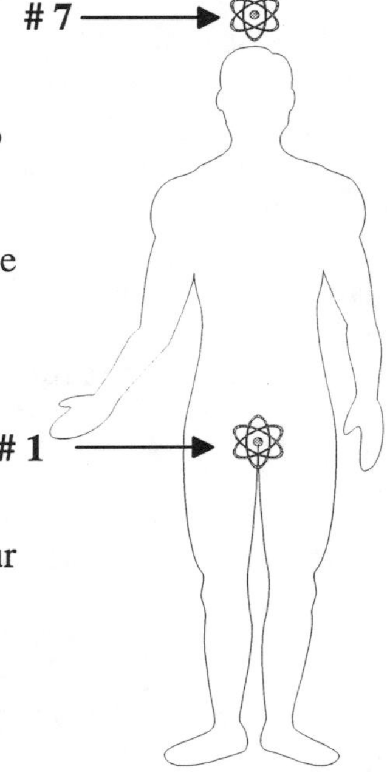


Sometimes I prefer to start with the head and work my way down through all the centers, or start at the feet and work my upward through the centers to the head. As you look through the description of the different functions each power center represents you decide which starting point you prefer.

I'll offer a brief summary of the glands or organs, the associated physical problems, and emotional growth that relates to each power center and what they symbolize for your overall health. Then how to work with them effectively in order to realize the benefits of this work.

The hand position to use is primarily **Drawing In**. The places to hold your position will be indicated by *numbered stops* to cover all the Power Centers for a total of *ten stops*. For a few stops the Putting In position will be mentioned as an alternate choice.

The position to use for the first Power Center is:

**Drawing In** at:

## Power Center #1:

There are two stops to make in this region. The area for Power Center #1 includes from the feet up to the top of the legs so you will have actually two stops in order to cover this whole area.

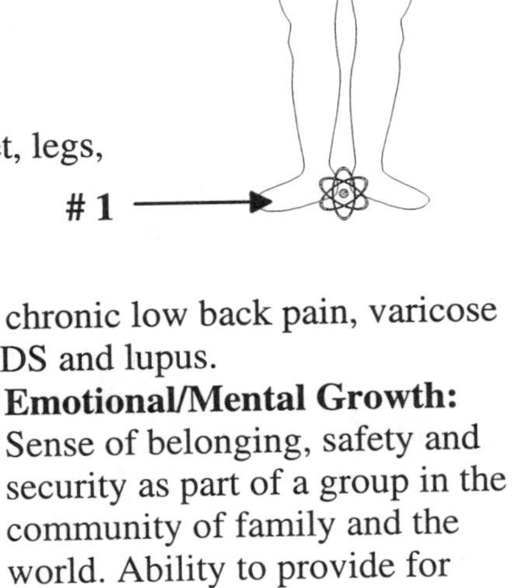


**Stop #1**: Over the feet. Hold just above the feet about 2-3 inches.

**Stop #2**: Area over the groin just below the genital area.

- **Glands/Organs Effected:** Feet, legs, base of spine, rectum, over all support of body including the immune system.
- **Physical Problems:** Sciatica, chronic low back pain, varicose veins, immune disorders as AIDS and lupus.

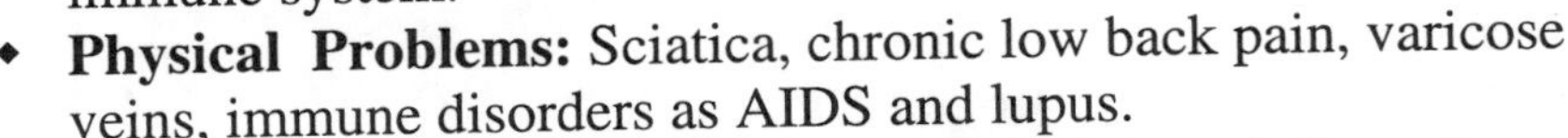

- **Emotional/Mental Growth:** Sense of belonging, safety and security as part of a group in the community of family and the world. Ability to provide for self.

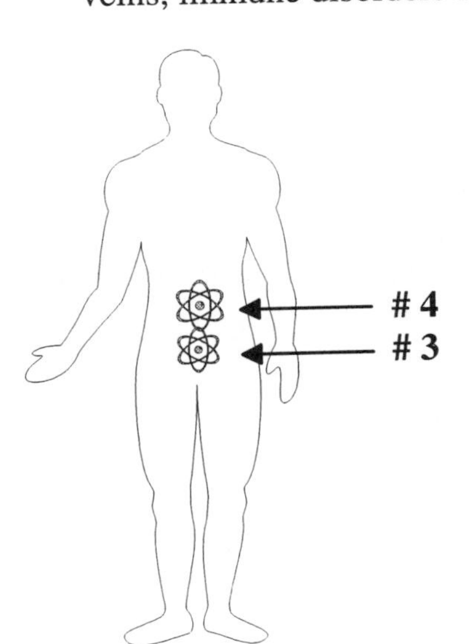


## Power Center #2

**Stop #3:** Hold one inch over the area below the navel, or lower pelvic area.

**Stop #4**: About one inch above the navel.

- **Glands/Organs Effected:** Pelvis, hips, lower vertebrae, large intestine, sexual organs, bladder.
- **Physical Problems:** Chronic lower back pain, sciatica, slipped disc, appendix, sexual and urinary problems as vaginal infections, and prostate.
- **Emotional/Mental Growth:** Peace, harmony and healthy ethics in relationship with others in the use of power, money and sex.

## Power Center #3

This area is where the center of your personal energy and vitality is generally considered to be stored and from there carried throughout your body.

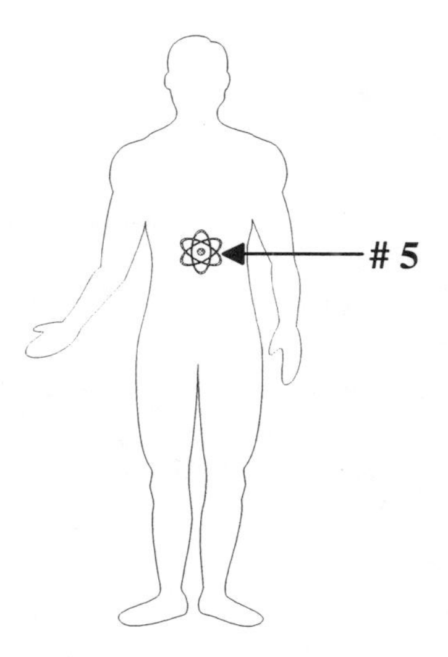


For the third Power Center, there is an option to use the Putting In position to add positive energy to this area. If vitality is low, this area can often be strengthened through positive energy. However, if a person is in general all around good health using positive energy of Putting In can result in excessive heat for the stomach area and for the entire body that can be uncomfortable. Asking the person if discomfort is the result of Putting In will largely be the way to know if Putting In or Drawing In should be used. Otherwise, since stress is the key factor we're after to reduce in a person's life, Drawing In is the hand position of first choice.

**Stop #5:** Solar Plexus region: Upper abdomen. About one inch below bottom of the rib cage.

- **Glands/Organs Effected:** Stomach, liver, upper intestines, kidneys/adrenal glands, gallbladder, pancreas, spleen, center of spine.

- **Physical Problems:** Intestinal/colon problems, ulcers, diabetes, liver disorders as hepatitis and Hemochromatosis, adrenal problems, arthritis, colds and flu.
- **Emotional/Mental Growth:** Trust, self esteem, confidence and respect and honor for self and others. Sense of joy, happiness, contentment, sexual assuredness, confidence/security in the future, ability to give love and forgiveness toward others.

## Power Center #4

**Stop #6:** Heart, middle of chest
**Stop #7**: Two inches above the heart

The heart area has an interesting gland called the thymus gland located above the heart at stop #7. This gland helps to govern the immune system's T-Cells (fighter cells) that fight infections in the body. Putting In is a good choice for stop #7 to assist in T-Cell production if low on positive energy. However, an over stressed immune system can also mean slow production of T-Cells. That would imply the need for Drawing In to reduce stress which in turn will help stimulate the thymus gland to produce T-Cells. It's a typical catch-22 scenario to know which position to use.

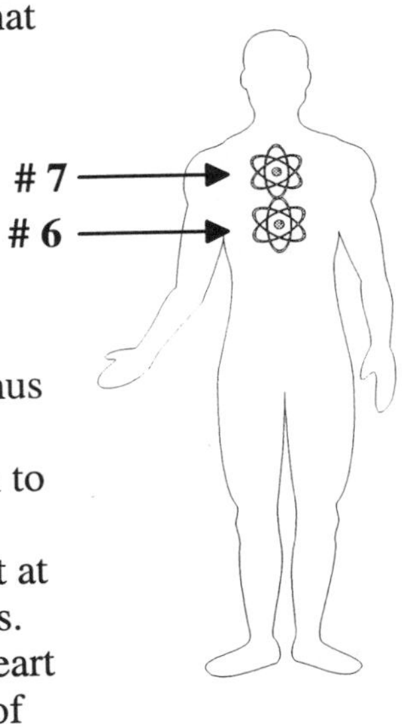

Putting In can also be used for the heart at stop #6 depending on the individual needs. The Receiver will notice an increase of heart rate with Putting In and a slowing down of the heart rate with Drawing In. Once again the best way to discover whether Drawing In or Putting is needed is by the response of comfort by the Receiver. You can also use both positions in covering this whole area using the Closed Loop position.

- **Glands/Organs Effected:** Heart, thymus gland, lungs, circulatory system, breasts, ribs, arms and shoulders.

- **Physical Problems:** Heart problems as congestive heart failure, allergies/asthma, pneumonia, emphysema, bronchitis, cancer of lung and breast, circulation problems, upper back, shoulders.
- **Emotional/Mental Growth:** Ability to give and receive love especially towards self, forgiveness/letting go of the past, humility, modesty, generosity.

Remain in the Drawing In position for the remaining stops along your route.

## Power Center #5

Stop #8 Throat

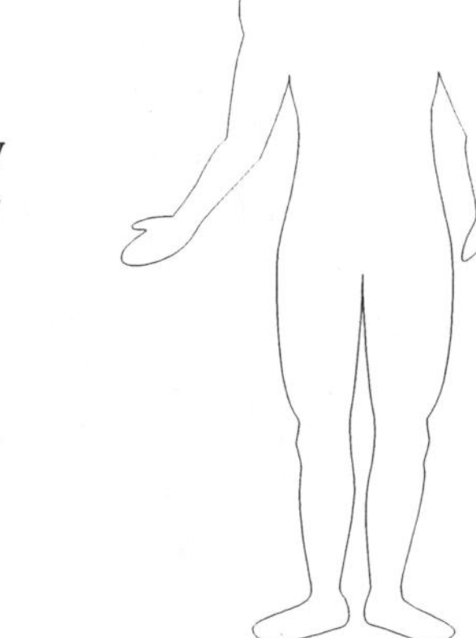


Generally speaking, (a throat pun) the throat area represents energetically the growth in our lives to speak up for ourselves. Complications in this area spill over to the heart region and back up again by representing struggles in not being able to express how we feel.

- **Glands/Organs Effected:** Throat, thyroid/parathyroid, neck, mouth/gums/teeth.
- **Physical Problems:** Chronic throat/mouth/gum problems, jaw joint complications, thyroid, scoliosis, addictions.
- **Emotional/Mental Growth:** The will and strength to live. Holding beliefs of personal power in overcoming obstacles. Decision making capabilities, personal expression of creative ideas, hopes and dreams. Personal sense of hope, lightness and buoyancy. This area is the center where we both begin and or overcome disease.

## Power Center #6

Stop #9 : Forehead, between eyes.

- **Glands/Organs Effected:** Brain, eyes, ears, nose, pineal gland, pituitary gland, thalamus, hypothalamus, overall nervous system.
- **Physical Problems:** Strokes, neurological problems, seizures, brain tumors, blindness, deafness, learning disorders.
- **Emotional/Mental Growth:** Ability to see truth as it is not for what we want it to be whether about ourselves or the world. Open to new ideas, ability to see ahead by circumstances of the present. Open to challenges of present knowledge in order to grow and learn from experiences. Having vision. Growth of wisdom, sense of higher intuition, thinking and reasoning. Sense of being connected to the Divine and our participation in the universe at large.

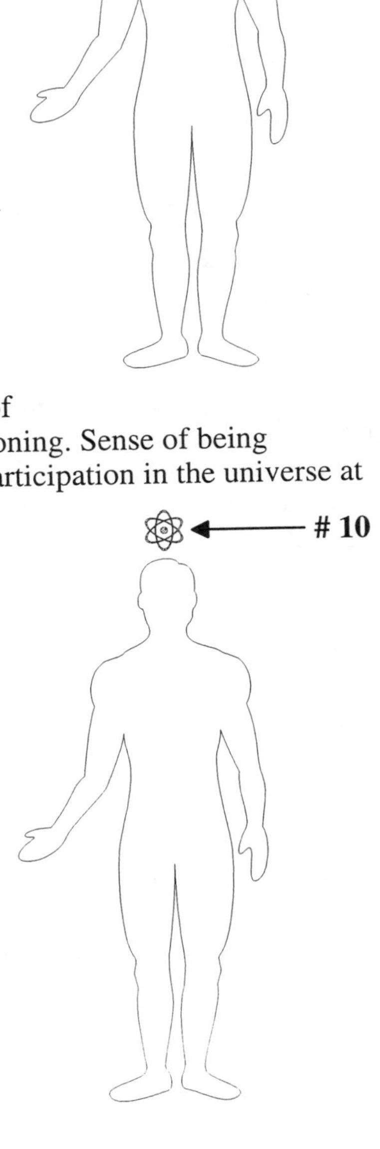


## Power Center #7

Stop #10: Top of Head

- **Glands/Organs Effected:** Skin, muscular, skeletal, and nervous system.
- **Physical Problems:** Chronic fatigue, Fibromyalgia, spiritual depression, bone problems, multiple sclerosis.
- **Emotional/Mental Growth:** Trusting connectedness to the Divine and with life. Development of values, meaning and purpose in life.

Now you know how to work with the Center Magnet and the individual sections.

Hold all positions until tingling or warmth stops or until the ten-minute time limit is reached.

## Overlapping Centers

You may notice that some physical and emotional areas cross over on each other like with the ability to love. The heart region is a center for love and forgiveness as well as the gall bladder in the third power center. The difference between them is the gallbladder is effected by the ability (or lack of ability) to let go of rage toward individuals that have done something harmful to us. The heart is effected by anger, a lesser intensity of the emotion of rage. Also, in the difference where the emotion is directed. The heart area is concerned more with ability to love and forgive the self, letting go of past personal mistakes and regrets, while the gallbladder deals specifically with about forgiving others.

Actually, all the power centers are about love. The individual areas represent stages of growth in how we learn to use power in choices of love or fear or hate; either we build ourselves and others up, or tear down and destroy. Wave Therapy can assist growth in love by helping to unmask and release negative energy (bad in this case) and allow for positive energy (good) to manifest in life.

## Working Whole

The seven power centers all overlap each other linked together as a working whole. Where energy is blocked in one emotional center the centers above or below will also be involved to some degree since they're neighbors. Since those centers also are linked to others all power centers will be effected in some way if just one is out of whack. Being how they're all connected, often while working with one power center there may be a physical reaction in a completely different area than you're presently working with.

Several areas will more than likely be involved in any particularly health problem since the power centers function as a whole.

For example:

- Immune disorders are generally categorized in power center #1 as a break down of safety and security in the world through negative tribal experiences as in relationships within a group, family unit or sense of belonging to the human family at large.
- Yet T-Cells are governed in the heart region at stop # 7, overlapping between the will to live, in power center #5 at the throat area for stop # 8 and the will to love the self in power center #4, for stop #6 at the heart region.
- Power Centers #5 of the will, and #4 for personal love of self, are both influenced by a sense of belonging as in power center #1. The first power center is influenced full circle back to #7, in the sense of belonging involving personal value, meaning, and purpose of life in our connection to the divine.

See how they all can work together? This may all seem overwhelming to learn in trying to connect them all together, but no need to despair in figuring out what to do. The first rule of thumb is simply start at one end of the body you prefer, either at:

- Power Center #1 at the feet, or
- Power Center #7 at the head, and
- Work your way through the stops.

Working with all the power centers in this way covers the whole of the Receiver's energy field to assist healing in the related emotional, physical and spiritual well being.

For the person who has a concern to work with like a bladder problem, there are two ways to go about finding which related power centers need assistance and other areas effected that require attention.

The first way is:

- The person (Receiver) tells you where their problem is located by telling you the problem is "In this area" or names the body area or organ.

The second way is:

- Scan the body for blocks and leaks to energy.

# Step #5

Usually after completing the seven power centers I move on to go hunting for areas that need a little extra attention. This is a good move to do during or at the conclusion of any session if time permits. Hunting for areas that need extra attention is worked through the. . .

## Body Scan (the dessert)

The Body Scan (or Spot Treatment) is a wonderful and helpful addition to a whole body work-up. It's like a dessert to top off the work you've already done.

The center magnet work-up helps supply needed energy that the body uses to send out to all the working parts of the body through the seven power centers. There are many more minor energy centers that are supplied energy from the main power centers. These area can be low on energy through blocks and leaks as well. If overall energy is low this may leave these other areas still in want of additional help, depending on the overall energy level. You or the person you're working with don't have to be able to identify these spots in order to work with them. The Receiver may not even be aware of the need. You can assist by finding and adding more energy to these areas manually. Simply follow the lead of your hands. That's what the Body Scan is for; searching those unknowns out.

If the Receiver doesn't offer information to you (or by this time too relaxed to say anything, or asleep) about where to start with where they think they may need additional help you can hunt for the spots needing attention by *body scanning*.

## How To Do The Body Scan ( Or Spot Treatment )

For this move you use The Drawing In position of your left hand as a **scanning tool**. The right Hand is again held out to your side with the palm facing to the floor in the Drawing In position.

Simply move around the body starting anywhere looking for **"hot spots."**

Hot spots are those areas that are giving you the signal that energy is needed and your hands respond to this communication by feeling the tingling, warmth, or sometimes even a cold sensation. When you get sensitive to the tingling or warm sensation in your hands, you can move your hand along above the surface of the body. When your hand begins to respond you have found a block or a leak. This is your clue to hang around a while and help out. You can work the whole surface of the body this way for a complete Body Scan.

## A Good Place To Start

- Start from the left side of the Receiver's body beginning at the left foot moving your left hand slowly anywhere along the left half of the body upward to the head, scanning for tingling or warmth sensations as you go.

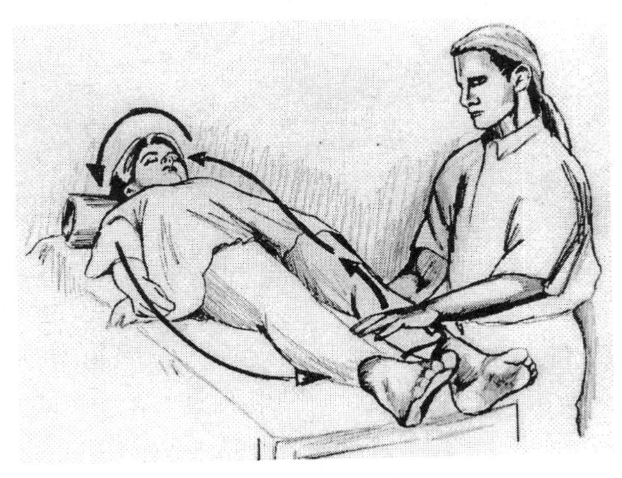

- Then you can begin again on the right side of the body and move downward toward the right foot in the same way.

When you find a hot spot, stop. Hold for up to ten minutes or until the physical sensations go away, whichever comes first, then move on to prowl around for another spot. If you find you aren't one who readily feels the energy experience, then ask the Receiver when he or she feels something and take the clue this is a place to stop. The Receiver can be your guide. Or, you can just go for what the Receiver says he/she would like to have you work on like a painful area and cut to the chase. However, there will always be hot spots where people have no idea that they're there.

You can start anywhere you like on the body, but I like to begin on the left side of the body. This path follows the natural course of energy flow around the body, pushing from the right side to the left. Beginning with hot spots you discover on the left side also helps to release blocks or leaks to the natural incoming flow of energy to flow more freely through its natural path.

You can start on the right side as well and move toward the left side if you prefer.

## The Closed Loop And The Body Scan

During the body scan, when you reach the head you can remain in the Drawing In position for any hot spots you discover around the head or perform the Closed Loop position, which ever you choose. The same goes for any hot spot you discover throughout the body. You can always switch to the Closed Loop position. It will bring about the effectiveness of both positive and negative magnetic influences of the power of life to an area. This is especially welcomed at joint areas, should you find hot spots in places such as the knees and elbows.

There is no rule needed here of which position to choose. Go by what you think may work the best. As you continue to do this work you will get a "feel" for what the body needs. Trust the feeling and go with it.

## Step #6

To finish off a whole body session there's a nice touch I like to add that seals your work.

## Sealing Your Work

After you are finished with the Body Sweep, Polarity Balancing, the Center Magnets and the Body Scan, you can do what I call "sealing your work." Sealing your work is done with a move that is a grand version of the Closed Loop position. It's easy to do.

## How To Do It

1. Stand to the right side of the Receiver at the center of the body and extend your arms out over the center of the body.
2. Hold the left hand facing toward the top of the head and the right hand facing toward the feet.
3. Hold for as long as you like or feel comfortable.

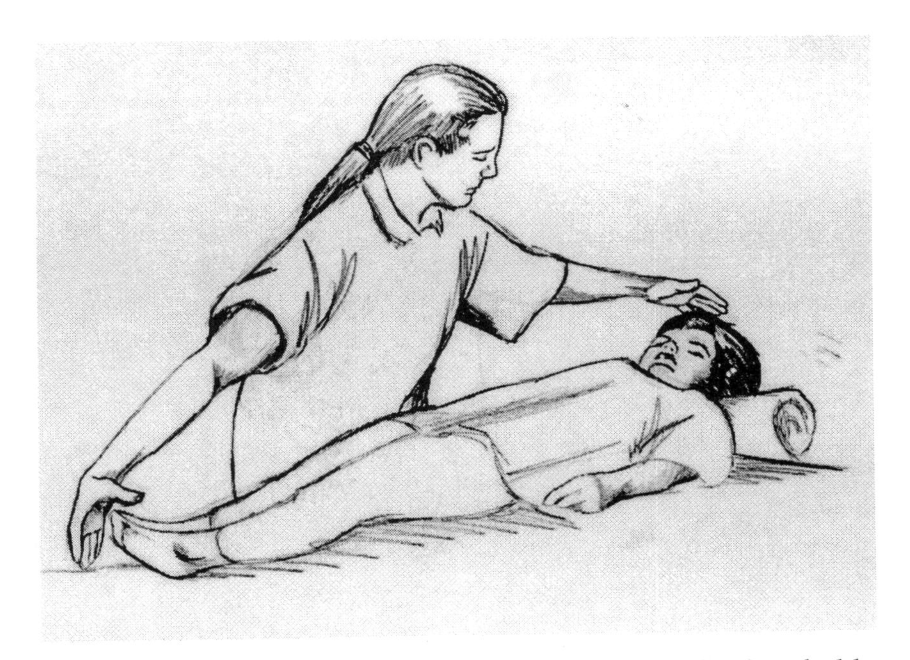

Most people's over-all body height will make it difficult to hold your hand at the bottom of the feet. Simply back away from the body and hold the position with palms facing toward the head and the feet. You will still effect the energy field just the same.

Hold this position until you feel it's time to stop. Usually a minute or two is enough. This seems to be a nice ending for both the person you're working with and for you. It's not only like a sign off to your work but it also ends the session with adding additional strength to the polarizing of the whole body magnet. It puts in energy at the feet with the right hand and draws in energy up toward the head with the left hand.

One of the reasons I prefer doing this position from the Receiver's right side is because of the opposites attract rule.

- The bottom of a person's body at the feet is over all negative. Since the right hand of the Giver is positive (+) the flow of energy of the positive hand (+) to the negative feet (-) is natural in nature.
- The top at the head is overall positive (+) in polarity and with the negative energy of the left hand (-) of the Giver, along with the positive of the right hand makes a complete natural Closed Loop over the body.

If you feel standing on the left side has benefits, then do so. Ask the person you're working with "What's going on?" or maybe, "What does that feel like?" That's a question I ask a lot. If you both like what you hear then stay with what you're doing. If there is a negative response, then switch sides.

When you're finished. . .

- Give your person a nice pat. You're done!

Now that you've learned all the positions and movements to do a whole body work-up let's pull them all together and list the moves in order.

### Summary Of Whole Body Work-Up

1. The Body Sweep
2. Polarity Balancing (The Wave or Family Version)
3. Grounding
4. The Seven Power Centers
5. Body Scan (or Spot Treatment)
6. Sealing (Head to toe Closed Loop)

### Optional Body Sweep

After a whole body work-up you can add an additional body sweep. It can be a good time to do this for much energy "debris" may have been loosened up from inside the body and worked its way to the surface during the session. So, naturally you can assist the person to clean off some more "bad energy."

You can perform this move either by again doing the full stand-up version of the Body Sweep, or the Receiver can continue to stay where he or she is and you can perform a mini-version of it. I've found that most people are so relaxed that to ask them to stand up again and wait while you perform twelve circles around their body is a little bit too much to ask. So I do a simple one on them while they're lying down and comfortable.

### Mini Body Sweep

What I do, is start at the head, with palms facing down and do a short outward grabbing stroke from the center magnet line outward to both sides of the body for a series of stops that work all the way from the top of the head to the bottom of the feet. The grabbing motion is just like what is done for the whole Body Sweep to pick up and throw lingering energy debris off to the sides.

### Here's How You Do It.

1. Start at the top of the head. Hold your hands on the center line of the body with palms facing the Receiver.
2. Then, as you do with the Body Sweep, cup the hands and with a grabbing motion, scoop the air like you're picking up something and with a quick move, grab it, flick it off and away from the body.
3. Move down about a hand's length and repeat. Do this all the way down to the feet. How many times is up to you. I usually do this about three times.

Now to show you how to apply a shorter version of a whole body work-up. The shorter version is ideal for those with limited time or for those who would like a quick overall boost or maintenance work.

## The Short Version

Here's a list of steps to complete a short version of a whole body work-up. This version takes about fifteen minutes to complete. It takes shorter time mostly by reducing the amount of attention given to work with the Power Centers by using only one hand move; the Closed Loop. The grounding and scanning steps are both optional.

## Whole Body Short Version

1. The Body Sweep
2. Polarity Balancing
3. Center Magnet (Closed Loop Version)
4. Seal

Perform the Body Sweep and Polarity Balancing moves the same as you would for the whole body version. The major difference will be in working with the Center Magnet.

Holding a Closed Loop position covering the length of the center magnet adds both negative and positive energy of the power of life to all parts of the body at the same time. Moving energy up and down this pathway through the center of the body supplies energy outwardly through the seven Power Centers feeding all the major organs and glands of the body. Working with the center magnet helps supply any needed energy to weakened areas of the organs and glands that have occurred through blocks or leaks of energy helping to balance out the entire functioning of the body.

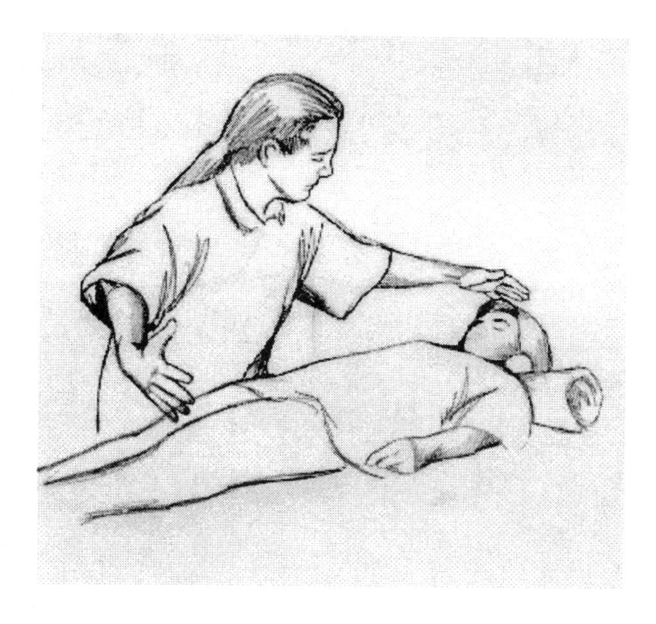

## How To Do It

1. Stand on the person's right side.
2. Place your left hand at the top center of the Receiver's head one to three inches away, not touching, palm facing downward toward the feet.
3. Place your right hand between the legs below the groin area from a distance of about one to three inches toward the feet with the right palm facing toward your left hand.
4. Hold the position ideally for two-three minutes or however long you discern a good flow of energy has done it's job. That sensation can be in the stopping of tingling in both hands, or an equal pressure feeling like the balloon sensation or you may just know by intuition. If your arms get tired give them a break, then continue when ready.

This may seem too simple and it is to perform but don't be mislead by the simplicity of it. This is a very powerful move you're doing. Why? I'm glad you asked. . .

What's going on (biologically) is that you're moving fresh new energy (physic-ally) through the Receiver's entire **endocrine system**. All the glands that produce all the hormones that regulate the body are positioned within the body between your hands during a Closed Loop of the center magnet. They're being bathed in a flow of energy that moves to them through the sexual organs, the lower and upper intestines, the kidneys, stomach, the spleen, gallbladder, the liver, heart, lungs, throat, and the brain. . .everything.

Since this is such a powerful move, you can also add this step into a whole body work-up if you like. A good time to add it is after completing work with all the Power Centers. It works like a balancing seal smoothing out energy flow between the Centers. I usually hold the position for about one minute if I'm working with the full version.

- After you have completed the Closed Loop of the Center Magnet hold the Sealing position, and you're done.

There you are. . .the short version of the whole body work-up!

After a whole-body work-up using either the long or short version it's time to take care of yourself.

Now it's time to. . .

## Wash Your Hands

As with all work you do, it can be a good idea to wash your hands thoroughly in cold running water when you're done.

Some believe that in the washing of your hands excess energy or debris is "washed off." There are those who say if you don't do this, you're in danger of keeping debris in your field that has been magnetized to your own field. This *can* be true. My approach now is that energy flowing through me after a session is so strong that it continues for a while to keep cleaning my own system out.

When I first started Wave Therapy, I was religious about washing my hands. I even kept a bowl of water on a table next to where a session was being worked and rinsed my hands often when I felt them getting "full."

Now, I hardly ever wash my hands. I have never gotten sick from taking on someone else's disease by not washing. There are times when I feel like doing it, so I do. My arms up to my elbows feel "contaminated," so I wash. I'm of the opinion that the focus of the attitude is what's important here. So, if you feel like washing by all means do so. If you believe you may pick something up by not washing your hands then "wash them puppies."

During a session sometimes your hands can get a full feeling to them. The way to get rid of this sensation if choosing not to wash your hands is to flick your hands so that your fingers sort of snap, snapping off the feeling. It works. Otherwise, keep a bowl of water handy. Dipping your hands in the water will also get rid of the full feeling. I use a metal bowl, with a drop of essential oil in it called In-tuit. A wonderful mixture made up of a flower essence that has a quite pleasant fragrance to it that's refreshing. It's not necessary to have the oil, I just like to use it. It's said to have properties about it that come from the energy field of a plant that assists in balancing energies. Whether it does or not I still like the stuff. You can get this essential oil from Dr. Norm Shealy at Self Health Systems, Brindabella Farms, Route 1, Box 216, Fairgrove, Missouri, 65648.

Or order some from me directly.

I use this wonderful fragrance in a spray bottle mixed with water. I spray the room before and after each session to freshen up the room.

I also use a little bit of incense before I get to work. Sandalwood is good. It's said by some to have properties in it that help clear up the "bad vibrations" that may come off people during such energy work. Whether that's true or not either, I don't know. I do know that I like the fragrance, and so do the people I work with. So I consider that it helps to promote a good attitude when the room smells so good. So, before and after each session I walk around the room with a lit incense stick in my hand waving it around, filling the room with its sweet odor. It's also a time of opening prayer for me as well, to focus on the work we're about to do and an opening of myself to the love of God that enhances the flow of the power of life that maintains balance and harmony. It's my way.

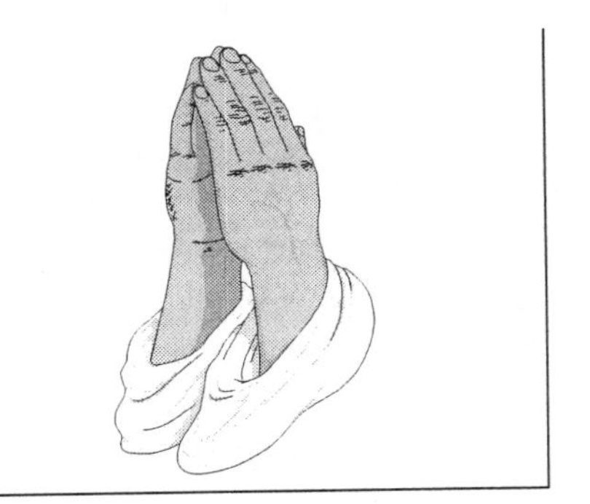

After a session there is another thing you can do that may help in cleaning out any sense of becoming clogged yourself with bad energy.

## A Self-Cleaning Position

- Hold both arms out to your sides at shoulder height.
- Hold the left hand facing up and the right hand facing down to the earth. Just like the Putting In position, only both arms are parallel to the floor.

Allow for a few minutes of energy flow to work its wonders for you. If you like, imagine fresh new energy coming through your left hand and cleaning you out as it moves through the right hand carrying anything you don't want out of your system. It's doing this anyway by the law of physics of magnetism. Since energy follows thought your imaging will have your thoughts move that energy as the energy follows it. You can also try picturing any dark or black stuff you may perceive as debris energy to be picked up by your thoughts and carried out. A very handy attitude to have toward any disease as well.

## Using Images

So many documented cases have shown that people having disease, image something eating up or carrying the disease out of their bodies. I read where one individual suffering from cancer used a Pac-man image, the little guy in the video game that went "wuka wuka wuka" through his route in a maze eating up little dots in the road along the way. A lady told me recently she uses the sink cleaning brush guy seen on a commercial to clean up cancer in her body. It worked for her, so if you get a favorite image to use that helps, try it and see how it works.

Images are not some metaphysical mumbo jumbo. Images are simply a language of pictures, something your subconscious mind of the soul and spirit use as commands or instructions to take action in the body. Dreams represent a whole different world whose culture of language use images to get a message across from the subconscious to the conscious mind to communicate. Images are tools in Wave Therapy you can use to get a message across for healing.

This is part of the nonphysical reality of our lives that we often don't give much attention to in a world of physical needs. The nonphysical world in reality is just as important to us as the physical. Such thing as emotions, ideas, thoughts, beliefs, and the invisible effects of magnetism are all nonphysical realties that effect our health.

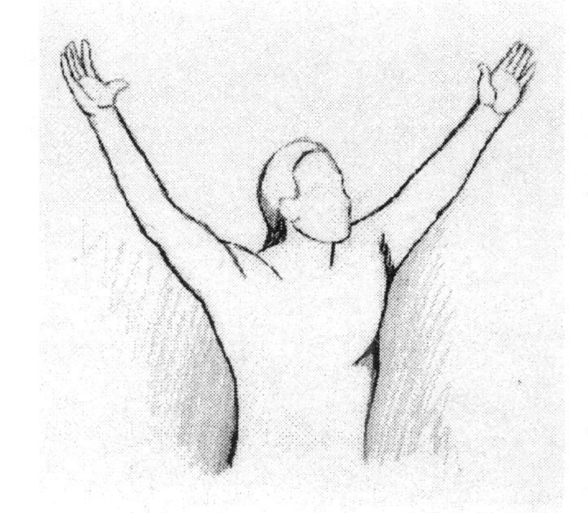

## Another Self Cleaning Position

There is one more self-cleaning position I'd like to offer. I hold this position before and after a whole body session, where I. . .

- lift both hands, palms facing upward as to the heavens.

This positions for me is an open heart expression to God of praise and thanksgiving for the power of life that flows from the Divine, through me and to the ones I work with. It's a Closed Loop expression of giving and receiving love. It's also a physical expression of humility and an offering of myself to the greatness that the Divine offers in working power through love. However you would like to think of the gesture it can be very both uplifting and calming.

With that, I'm going to grab the donkey by the tail and discuss another benefit of Wave Therapy: How to help others in their healing process who are actually not in the same room with you. The next section will be on taking Wave Therapy a step farther in working with people over long distance.

# PART III

# Wave Therapy

## Long Distance Healing

# LONG DISTANCE HEALING

## *Intercessory Prayer*

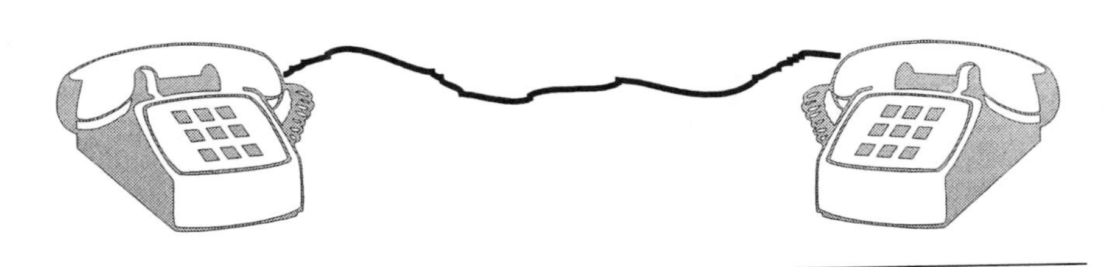

The subject of assisting other persons to heal who are not in the same room with you can be a tad too far for some people to consider, much less a possibility. Yet most of us attempt the process whether we actually believe it will work or not. That process I'm speaking of is prayer. We all have times when we may have someone in our lives in need of help who just may not be where we  are physically located at the time. So thus, this section.

It's true. You can apply the techniques of Wave Therapy with those who are not present, with their permission and consent of course. Not only is it good manners but mutual agreement helps the process to work better. Long Distance work can be affective for those who don't know you're working on their behalf for healing, however, I have also found mutual agreement is one of the elements for long distance or remote healing to be more affective for some. There are a few other elements that are helpful  to consider that will be given attention to in this section. Well also talk about dealing with some of the common obstacles to considering working with this powerful approach to healing.

### What Is Long Distance Healing?

Long Distance healing for me is really **intercessory prayer;** asking for assistance or intervention on behalf of another person for healing in any area of life.  In fact the act of working Wave Therapy in any of the hand positions is in act of intercession where one person is assisting another person with a problem where they have become weak in overcoming the health problem on their own.

Long Distance healing in action is really no more unusual than what goes on in prayer where a person is communicating with the Divine Creator. I tend to call the process of working with the physical hand movements of Wave Therapy as ***physical prayer***. To me it's a movement of visible faith by stepping out physically in taking action to activate the flow of the power of life.

One obstacle in long distance healing is considering the idea of visibility. When applying hand positions of Wave Therapy the person is physically with you and once you have come to understand how the process works in a close environment, adapting the work for long distance is just another step. Using the hand positions in Wave Therapy in placing them around the body of someone in your presence is an action both the Giver and Receiver can see. However in prayer, the one you may be praying for is also not visible in your presence and the Giver is not seen either by the Receiver. The One being prayed to is not visible in your presence either. It seems to me geography is the problem in question concerning long distance not the power available to assist in healing.

So, to get over the stumbling block of geography in considering long distance healing for someone here is a consideration to think about.

## Geography And The Divine

Geography is a term used to describe the place of a physical object. A town's geography can be located on a map. You can count on it to be there in the same place. That is unless a tornado moves the town. The same goes for any physical thing as a spoon, a glass, a car, a continent, you and me. We always have a physical place we are located at.

What about God? Where is God?

Traditionally we say God is everywhere. Wave Therapy approaches the idea that the invisible energy of the divine creative God flows everywhere in order to sustain life and hold all things together in balance and harmony. We can sense and feel that energy between our hands and body as we work the hand positions.

The geography of God is that the divine is everywhere all at once. Something we obviously are not used to ourselves. Not only is the divine presence of energy available flowing with the power of life through your hands where you are at now but also with any person around the world. That's because the geography of this divine energy presence is not limited to one spot like we are being physical in nature.

In long distance healing the idea is that the presence of God is with you, with me, with everyone no matter where we are at. For those familiar with the world wide web, the internet, it roughly demonstrates the same thing. I can dial into the world wide web by my computer and connect to any other computer in the world because of the web of communication lines of computers being connected to one another.

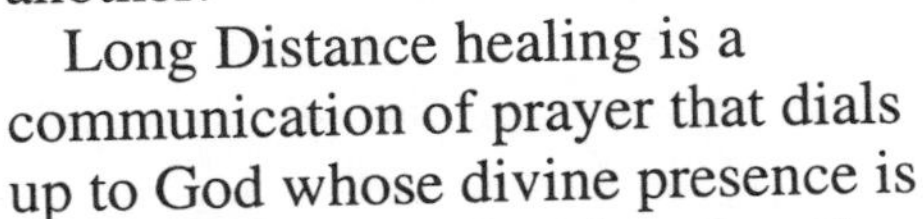

Long Distance healing is a communication of prayer that dials up to God whose divine presence is everywhere and all at the same time connected to everyone. By the same act of faith (taking action) it takes for you to stretch out your hand in a Closed Loop position to work on relieving pain in someone's knee in the room with you the same thing can be done for someone across the miles. In other words, there is no distance in prayer due to the interconnecting presence of the divine creative energy of the power of life of God who is everywhere.

## No Distance In Space

Working with long distance healing involves challenging the general concept of being limited to space. Here is probably the hardest concept to grasp about this kind of work. You don't have to understand it for it to work. It works anyway. For those who have an interest, I've come to find out that there is no distance in space between people. It doesn't matter how far away someone else is. You still impact each other.

## A Love Triangle

Let's look at it this way.
Imagine a triangle of persons.

1. God (The one with the power)
2. You (The Giver or Intercessor of power), the
3. Person (The Receiver, receiving the power)

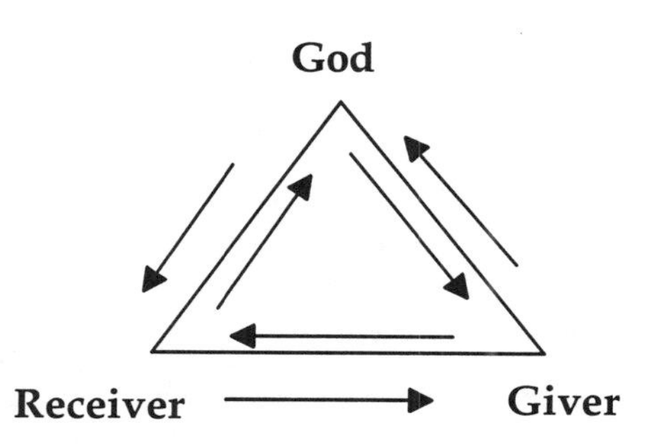


The two people in this scenario are physical and have a nice physical spot where you'll both be. Now God is wholly spirit. He doesn't have a "spot" He's bound too. No body. Being wholly spirit has the privilege of being everywhere at once. When you link up in prayer (invisible communication) with God you are in touch with Him. He is also in touch with everything from one end of everything to the other end of everything, if there is an end to everything. God is already in touch with the Receiver. Think of it as a satellite connection. Prayer directs the Giver's intention "upward" to God for healing, and God directs His intention "downward" to the Receiver.

We have seen that in nature the will of the creator for health and wholeness is demonstrated in the laws of nature for all things to be in balance and harmony. With the hand technique of healing we have seen this Will in operation. With long distance healing the same Will or intention to heal is operating. So, actually the intention is already there for all parties concerned, but it's the act of opening the lines of communication that begins the process of the power of life to flow. That's one way of looking at how there is no distance really.

We're all familiar with communication with people that aren't there in the room with you, yet are still able to get in touch with one another. An example is a phone connection. I pick up the phone and call someone. Their phone rings, they pick the receiver up and say "hello?" and you respond. The line between you connects your communication and you can talk to each other like you're both in the same room.

Connecting to one another across the distances of space works the same way in the spiritual realm. You connect with God who is your line to everywhere and the other person connects and you can communicate the power of God like you're both in the same room. A conference call!

Like with participating in any phone conversation one person has got to pick up the phone to make the call, the other has to answer, otherwise there is no communication; the lines are closed. So the first step in getting anywhere with long distance healing work is you have to pick up the phone. In fact is was actually over the phone that I experienced my first attempt at long distance healing.

### My First Try

A wonderful lady friend of mine called up one day to talk about meeting for a session to see if the therapy would help with calming down her pain. She was having a terrible attack of arthritis in her hand.

For a moment I considered the concept of no distance in space and took the plunge.

"We don't have to meet Marge. We can work together now over the phone."

"What?" she asks.

And before she could say anything else, I said to her,

"Hold up your hand."

I paused a second for her to do it.

"Are you holding your hand up?" I asked.

I heard her say, "yes" with a little hesitancy.

"Good. Now hold it there for a little bit. Now. . ."

I held up my hands, holding the receiver by bending my head down to it holding it in place on my shoulder. I imagined her hand was between my hands and I continued to talk with her about stuff; her husband and so on. We talked for a couple of minutes not ever referring to her holding up her hand or what I was doing on my end. After a few minutes of conversation I entered the question.

"Well, Marge, how's your hand doing now."

She had forgotten all about it while we were talking.

"Why. . .Why all the pain is gone! This is too strange to confess too but I have to! I don't have any pain at all, Sam."

"Well good!"

And that was that.

## How To Do It

To work long distance healing begins first with taking the leap to try. Once you've cleared that obstacle there are two ways to choose to go about the healing process. I'll present two "plans" to go about it:

1. **Plan #1: Using the hand positions**
2. **Plan #2: Not using the hand positions**

I started with a simple hand position effort, then graduated to doing whole body work sessions, to discovering that no hand movements can be just as effective if not more powerful in gaining results.

# PLAN #1

## Using The Hand Positions

The hand position that I have ended up using the most is the Closed Loop. However, I have performed an entire session on people over long distance using all five positions and movements. Some obstacles to working long distance healing are:

- You feel stupid
- Getting the courage to suggest to someone to try this out with you
- Once you do start you get tired of focusing on what you're doing because no one is there

I've done simple work for aches and pains where mostly I keep the sessions down to about ten to fifteen minutes. However with long distance I have found there is no time limit on how long you can or have to work with someone. It's one of those things of however long you can hold out. As you get accustomed to it and learn more of your own insights through practice even the amount of time involved can be shortened.

To get you started I'll offer the steps I take to initiate a long distance partnership with someone. These are only tools I've found along the way as guidelines concerning long distance healing. You may find other ways that work better for you. If you do, great! These suggestions are not rules that if you miss following them means you've messed up and you're not meeting some requirement for healing to happen. They're merely ways I use to help both myself as the Giver and for the Receiver to get in a better environment to encourage the healing process.

The first step I consider to be a good link to get things started. Actually it's no different than when you're working with someone in person where you both have decided together in agreeing to take action.

## ***Step One***

### Agree On A Time

When someone you agree to try this out with over distance, like in being across town from each other,

- Agree on a time when you will "meet."

This is so you will be working together; that harmony part of the wholeness in health.

For people I work with in this way we work out a mutual time where we both have time and a place where we can each be alone. This helps for focusing attention on what you're doing for both the Giver and the Receiver. Your spirit and their spirit and God's spirit will be meeting together across time and space to join together as a working team.

## Step Two

### Lay Down

Then I suggest that he or she lay down, relax and focus attention on receiving the power of life from God. Then watch for any changes.

## Step Three

### Keep It Simple

In doing long distance assistance to heal, there is no need to work up your imagination that you are "sending" healing energy. Or, that you have to imagine you're there with the person. That's way too much work. Trying to imagine you're somewhere else can be a strain. No need to do that. Keep it simple.

- Simply picture the body part of the person is there with you between your hands.

You can work all the Wave Therapy hand positions on the person as if they're right in the room with you.

- Imagine the person is in front of you physically while working the Body Sweep, the Body Balancing move, Closed Loop, Drawing In or Putting In. Even the Blood Cleanser move.

Attempting a whole body work-up over long distance can get tiring in trying to hold your attention for the time it takes because there is nothing in front of you, like a body to work on, just air. You may find your thoughts wonder easily without an actual body part to focus on. So, in using the hand movement plan I found I usually restrict myself to working with people with isolated aches and pains as in the knees, a headache, arthritis in a joint, and so on.

In wanting to work with more complicated health problems or even assistance for any request from someone to make changes in their life that aren't physical issues, working with plan #2, the no-hands long distance healing works well.

# PLAN # 2

## *Not Using The Hands Positions*

I personally have ended up going the route of not using the hands at all. It took trying out using the hands to find out that Wave Therapy does in fact work over long distance. Just like it took using the hands in the first place on someone at all to see that this method of assisting others to heal actually works.

My first experience at the no hands approach is an example of the difference of how less effort offers just as powerful results for healing.

The intention to heal is a powerful communion between yourself, another and God who I believe has intention that we be whole, in balance and in harmony as is displayed in nature.

### A Story

I got a call from a friend one day, who out of the blue was experiencing terrible pain in one of his feet. He wanted to ask me to work on him. He lived out of town, oh. . . about and hour and half away.

"What's the problem?" I asked. A good question.

"I've developed gout in my foot and it hurts really bad. What can I do?" He asks. "Can you help in some way long distance with the therapy you do?"

"We can give it a try." I briefly considered how we could go about this.

"Tell you what, let's meet together at one o'clock today. I'll work with you for an hour. So find a comfortable place to sit down and receive."

We agreed on the time, and I went off to work at the office.

Work that day was in helping to finish off building a fireplace area in a room we were renovating. It was in our warehouse downtown. Actually, it was going to be a fireplace and mid-stream it turned in to sort of an altar area where we were planning on having healing services. So I was hammering away and forgetting the time. When suddenly my hands lit up like a Christmas Tree. Energy was pouring out of them like a switch was just turned on. I had forgotten about our "appointment." I looked up at the clock on the book case next to the soon to be altar. It was straight up one o'clock. Robert was on time.

The sensations continued at full power for about forty five minutes while I continued to work away at measuring, cutting wood and hammering away the best I could. Then the feeling started to wane and finally quit. I looked up at the clock on the wall. It was two o'clock. The hour was up.

I forgot about it all during the rest of the day's pre-occupation with the building project and didn't think to call him till the next morning. When I called him he reported the pain had gone and the gout with it. The power went out to heal.

In this instance, I didn't sit around in determined focus to offer healing. Neither did I hold any particular position. I went on with the work at hand. The intention to be in the flow with God to Robert was there. That was all that was needed. His faith reached out over the miles and touched with mine igniting the flow of power of life to flow between us. God, Robert, and Me working as one. I didn't even remember which foot it was he needed help with. He just needed power to heal and that was enough.

In this experience I didn't hold any positions or perform any movements. It was the movement of power through a pure act of the magnetic power of faith. In the short run, the hand positions are tools to taking action. When you get in the flow of that you'll find as with this story the power behind the power of life is God himself, who requires only our being there to participate; being open and willing to participate in His will to heal that is moved through Divine love.

## Love Is Healing

After learning more how long distance works through the act of just "being there" there are times when working with a person in person, I end up just standing there next to him or her. I don't use any hand positions. What the person is really needing is direct experience of the healing power of love. To me all sickness is due to disharmony and imbalance that occurs through the lack of love. This may sound too simplistic of a viewpoint to consider on first thought. So here's how I see it.

I view God as Love. If love is experienced we experience God. In that meeting we contact the author of wholeness and harmony, which means health according the laws of biology and physics. So, I let love flow; From God, through me, to the person. I don't have to *feel* the love. What I feel is not the measure of what is received. What feelings I do focus on is opening myself up to releasing all fears that I may have that God is not there to help. Or, that I must be perfect in some way. Being perfect is something I don't have to do or can do. I do attempt to be as open and transparent as I can and expect that God will work through me in all the faults I possess. Holding no judgment against myself is the task in those moments. I just BE there. When I reach this place within me I'm in a better position to love myself. That opens me up to allow more love to flow directly from God through my spirit to the spirit of any person in need of the healing that comes through the harmony and balance of experiencing love.

I have another story to offer and it's about the art of Being. It demonstrates even further about the power of the mercy and love of God that is willing to reach out to touch and heal even while we are unaware of that intention going on in our lives.

## A Chaplains Visit

I was working as a hospital chaplain for the Veterans Administration in a clinical pastoral education program. As it happened I was working on the fine art of Being while visiting patients. My approach to pastoral care was to focus on an attitude within of being content with being myself with patients with whatever that could offer them. The attitude attempt was in not trying to be super chaplain by hoping to come up with some inspirational words of wisdom to help them see them through their crisis. In other words, not trying to feel important enough to warrant my being there working with the hospital staff in such simplicity.

On this particular day I wandered into a room with four patients.

Two beds on the north end and two on the south end of the room. I started on the left north side to offer initial greetings to everyone. After three hello's, how ya doing, and several kinds of responses I ended up with the fourth man on the south end, last bed. I was intending to stop with him anyway because he had requested a Bible from another chaplain who had visited him earlier that day. I was on a mission to deliver that Bible.

I found him working on putting together a plastic model of soldiers. He had a heart monitor on him that was displaying a read out of blips and lines on the monitor screen overhead. This room was for heart patients. But that didn't concern him much for the moment for he was intent on putting this model together. It appeared he was about done. In the spirit of practicing the art of Being I decided that spirituality was about two people finding common ground to build on and work a relationship from there. So, I took interest in his project.

We worked on it together and found some solutions to finish. Then he was ready to talk some more. I thought, "Well, now maybe he'll want to talk about spiritual concerns a bit since he asked for the Bible." But no, he started talking about the heart monitor. And talk and talk. We talked about all the lines, though neither of us knew what they meant. Only that they were different from the others in the room. It seemed to me we were babbling about nothing. The only thing it appeared was going on was that we were taking up time. After a while I began to wonder if he was avoiding something. He talked for thirty minutes about the monitors. Several times I attempted to bring the conversation to a close simply because I couldn't possibly think of another thing to comment on about monitors. Then suddenly he stops.

"Do they have a newspaper up at the desk?" he asks.

"I don't know, but I'll go ask for you," surprised at the abrupt turn of the conversation.

"I'll be right back." I leave to go look.

They had no newspaper. I returned to give him the news.

"That's OK, I'll just go downstairs to the lobby and pick one up there. Thanks."

"Sure. Well. . .have a good evening. I'll check with you tomorrow on how you're doing."

I could think of nothing else to say.

"OK, then."

I turn to leave as I see him pull the chair over I had been sitting on to use to stand up.

Now this part of the story may not seem like much. I didn't think so either. But the next day revealed a more interesting story behind it all. This is an exact duplication of my report to the head chaplain I submitted as part of the pastoral care program. The "C" stands for Chaplain; me. The "A" is for the patient's name. We kept identities of patients confidential so used initials.

1. C: Hi. How are you doing today? (Sit down on side of bed, next to him)
2. A: Oh good! (Big smile on his face)
3. C: That's good news.
4. C: Looks like you got your statue all put together.
5. A: Yep. It wasn't so bad taking it apart like I thought it would be. And I didn't need any glue.
6. C: Well, good for you.
7. A: Sorry about yesterday. I didn't mean anything by it.
8. C: (Surprised) What?
9. A: About keeping you here? I didn't want you to leave. I didn't mean anything by it.
10. C: That's fine. I liked talking with you.
11. A: As soon as you walked in I started feeling better. I didn't want you to leave.
12. C: What? (I hadn't a clue. To me the visit seemed quite unordinary for such a reaction.)
13. A: When you came in I just got better and better. That other Chaplain, uhmmm. . .the one with the black hair?
14. C: Chaplain A. . .(I thought that people seem to identify us all by our hair.)

15. A: He came in and prayed for me earlier. Then when you came in I started feeling better and better. . .Look!

16. A: (Starts swinging his left leg up and down.)

17. C: That's great! (I didn't have a clue what that meant. I didn't know there was a thing wrong with his leg.)

18. A: Do you notice anything missing?

19. C: (I look around. I don't notice anything particular.)

20. A: The wheelchair's gone. While you were here my leg kept getting better and listen. . .(swings leg up and down again) no more noise. My knee makes such a grinding and popping noise that guy over there could hear it clear across the room when I moved it. Couldn't ya? (Asks the man in Bed #1.)

21. C: (I look over to the man on my left and he's looking at me and nods his head, yes.) That's wonderful. What happened?

22. A: I dunno. I've had such pain in that leg for seven years I've had to use a wheelchair. But I just took that thing up to them after you left and told 'em, "You can just keep that thing. I don't need it anymore!"

23. C: Well, it certainly looks like God did a good thing for you.

24. A: He sure did!

25. C: Well, congratulations!

26. A: Yeah!

27. C: Well, you just keep getting better, all right?

28. A: Sure will!

29. C: (I'm so surprised I leave to go up to the nurses station. I'm standing there thinking about what just happened and A comes walking passed us.)

30. N: (nurse) Can you believe that guy? I've never seen anything like it. Look at him the way's he's walkin'.

31. C: Amazing isn't it?

## The Art Of Being

I tell you this story because it speaks of the power of Being. I didn't do piddly in intending to assist in healing for anything. In fact I was completely unaware anything good was going on during our conversation. All that was necessary was presence; of Being with the person.

You can read into this any other kind of Laws at work you would like to consider. What I do know is the power of God to heal was certainly working. This goes to show that the act of what seems to be doing nothing doesn't necessarily mean good things for healing aren't happening anyway. The act of doing comes out of our being; of who we are. You can only do out of who and what you are anyway. In this case I was who I was and the patient was who he was. We were working together unknowingly on a conscious level but still working together in invisible communion between ourselves and the will of God to heal.

In my work with people over long distance there are some things that are the same between the two styles of using your hands and not using your hands. There are some healthy attitudes that I would like to pass along. I'll mention a few beginning attitudes that are helpful for the healing process for both the Giver and the Receiver.

Working without hand movements maintains the same kind of participation in Plan Two of:

## The Receiver

1. Agreement of a meeting time.
2. Lying down, relax, and focus intention on receiving

For the Receiver an additional helpful attitude approach is one of

- Acceptance of love.

## A Time To Receive

Petition time for concerns of the Receiver is over for the moment. Now it's a time to expect answers are being given and a time to receive. One of the problems I believe in why there seems to be an imbalance in the asking and receiving arena is we do far more asking than is necessary. Someone who loves you does not require continual asking. Hearing once is enough unless the person being asked forgets the request. I don't think that's the problem here. I see the problem as the One who gives has his hand out to give, our hand to receive is usually not there. This is a time to receive so take the posture. It's an act of faith. Sit back, relax, and take in what comes.

## The Giver

For the Giver in this process, there is also an attitude adjustment to make that I have found helpful. With less physical action on the part of the Giver to focus on there still is a job to do. Mostly the job is in knowing your place in where the Giver fits into the healing process. Casting aside your fears of being the burden bearer in the process of healing is one of the Giver's main jobs. To help with this I'll offer my imaginary physics viewpoint of the healing process to consider that may be helpful in knowing your place.

## Knowing Your Place

Magnetically speaking the. . .

- Receiver is in the restful, relaxed, calm mode of negative influence (-).

- The Giver is in the positive, action, building up, strengthening mode of positive influence (+).

For no-hands long distance work you may not know what to do. That's the point. You don't do any physical hand movement. I usually just stand in place somewhere and determine that power is going out to heal. My focus is that whomever I'm working with, they are laying down and are ready to receive. I stand in place as the Giver where the power of life is flowing through from God to me to the person. Sounds too simple to be true doesn't it? Well then. . .

Let's go a little deeper now. Let's take a look at understanding how long distance healing may work according to some simple laws of magnetism.

# THE PHYSICS OF

# LONG DISTANCE HEALING

## *The Giver*

### The Giver Is Neutral

Though you are considered the Giver in the healing process you are actually a go-between, a neutral (0) observer in the process. In long distance healing more than ever you experience how much you are not the healer but the facilitator of the process of healing on behalf of another person. Your part to play is once again comparable to the process that goes on in a magnet.

For every magnet, just like your body, there is a positive and negative side. There is also a neutral point, a place where the positive and negative energy changes as it moves from one side or end to the other. This in-between place is always at the center of a magnet, just like the center of the earth. You may have not thought about it before but it's there.

On the front of the body the polarity is negative and the back it's positive. Somewhere in between at the center of the body the energy change from one polarity to the other. That's the neutral zone. [9]

---

9 In physics of magnetism, this neutral zone is called the Bloch Wall.

As the Giver in long distance healing you actually are the neutral player in the process. The more you simply BE, the better. The "being" is being in between positive and negative. Neither pushing or pulling, acting or resting. The attitude to develop to get in this position is however you can manage to discipline yourself to be an observer; to just be there.

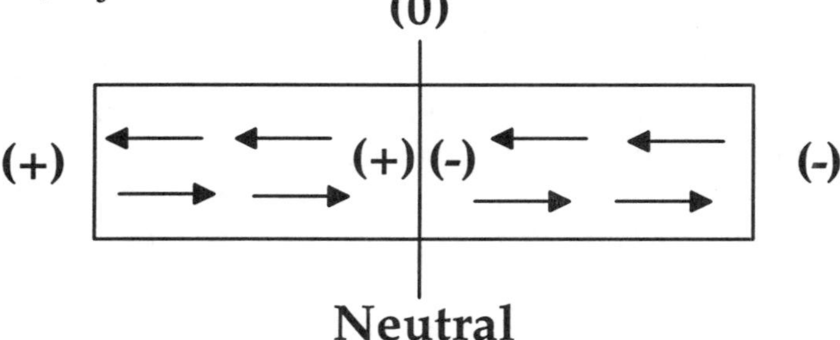


All of Wave Therapy practice is simply an act of your being there to assist another in their healing process. Long distance healing is carrying out the same principle with more attention (or less) to your role.

Your part to play involves the same magnetic influence in long distance healing as it is when working in person. Even the language of the hand positions can be adopted here to describe what's going on where:

- God acts as the Giver by Putting In (+, positive) and
- You act as the go-between (0, neutral) for the process.
- The Receiver is able to Draw In the healing (-, negative) power of life.

## The Physics Of Prayer

So. If you care to look at it this way the work of long distance healing can be a combination of the physics of the polarity of magnetism working in harmony with the spirituality of faith as an action through prayer. The whole process acts as a big Closed Loop.

- The request for assistance by the Receiver acts first as positive (+) for taking action. As the request for healing moves through the magnetic influence of faith, the request. . .

- Moves through you as the go-between, the intercessor. It changes at the center of our imaginary magnet to Zero.
- As the request moves toward God, the answer of giving the power of life becomes positive (+) as it moves back down the lines of communication to take action to heal.
- As the action to heal moves, through you, the neutral (0) Co-Giver, it once again changes as it passes to the negative healing mode (-) for the Receiver (-).

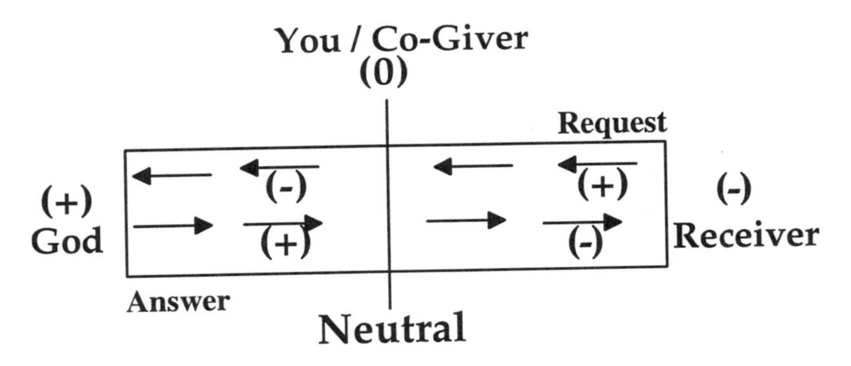


The attitude concerning your part is more important in recognizing though, that you are the initiator of the process. It's not you that heals. In faithful observance of how the polarities of a magnet works in nature the same principle will apply in knowing your place in the grand scheme of things for long distance healing. To summarize the way I see how the flow of the power of life moves in the healing process:

- **GOD, as Giver, gives the power of life (+)**
  It flows through
- **YOU, as co-giver (0-neutral)**
  as it passes along through you to the
- **Receiver (-)**

With that I give you a few helpful attitudes to begin with. Some highlights for the Giver are:

# Helpful Attitudes

## Helpful Hints For The Giver

- Direct attention as with all healing efforts that power belongs to God to heal.
- The Divine Creator's intention as displayed in nature is for balance and harmony. Wholeness is God's intention for all.
- Remain neutral about your efforts to heal. The effort of taking part of the healing process is sufficient. The act of BEing there is all the act of traditional faith it takes to starting the healing process in motion.
- The presence of God is with the other person already. You do not make that happen. The two of you, the Giver and Receiver are opening up to the kingdom of God to answer the prayer. . . NOW!
- You are the center, the neutral zone or pathway which between the receiver and God for which the healing energy flows through to get to the Receiver. You are the intercessor.
- As the neutral one, offer no judgments.

We are used to offering reasons and judgments why people get sick. There are reasons, and the basis of illness has been discussed here that have to do with the balance and harmony of energy within and around us as one of those reasons. In intercessory long distance healing the why's are not the concern. It's action that's the key; taking the leap to believe that when asking for healing, expecting that something is being done now is actually happening. Remaining neutral takes the burden off trying to act as God, remaining in the hands of the One who gives the power of life.

## Helpful Hints For The Receiver

For the Receiver I have found it helpful to:

- Have a goal in your healing process.
  You already have an idea of what you're wanting or you wouldn't be participating in a long distance session (or any

Wave Therapy work) but it's helpful to list one to three things you're looking for changes in. Don't make this a huge list to begin with. If it's a physical problem then list it. If it's a job, relationship needs or any subject you may be having anxiety, worry, fear, or guilt involved, list it. Have a clear goal in mind of where you want to be.

- Relax.
  Take a few good deep breaths and let the air out slowly. Pay attention to where there is stress or tension in the body and let it go. Tension caused by your thoughts will start to lessen as your body relaxes. Relaxing puts you into a better receiving mode for healing.

- Allow for love.
  Get over any logical reason why you shouldn't be healed, whatever the need is whether physical, mental, or spiritual. This is a time to let love of the Divine do its work. As I mentioned before I believe that the lack of love is the lack of the presence of God, therefore the lack of balance and harmony. Let love re-align you like re-aligning and balancing the wheels of a car. Part of allowing for love to enter is in letting go of judgments against yourself. A sense of judgment can be revealed in the attitude that you don't deserve to be better. To help let that attitude go, this is a time to take the risk to receive the attitude of God revealed in nature that all things are meant to be in balance and harmony. That means God's will is for all to be well. That means you too.

- Pay attention.
  What happens, happens. No telling what may occur for you through long distance healing work. For instance you may need a physical healing and not see any action right off. Instead an attitude change occurs. Or, insight to change the way you live that will help the healing process. Don't insist on the results any more than the Giver doesn't insist but remains neutral. We all have our ideas of what we want and we usually want it NOW! What you want to have happen may not happen. . .just yet. So pay attention to the process

where it may lead you in your healing journey and follow where it takes you.

These are some highlighted attitudes that are helpful. These are a few primers to begin with and expand upon. Healing is a process of becoming whole. So watch the process and participate in it.

## Less Is More

I would like to add another helpful hint to assist in being able to keep focus on a balanced attitude of your place during the long distance healing process as the one being the intercessor. My tactics may seem a bit strange in what I suggest here for it may seem like I'm giving less focus rather than keeping it. For my approach works opposite than the way as Americans we tackle life and that is,

- Less is More.

I have found that physical movement on my own part while working the long distance healing process is helpful to keep my mind distracted from wanting to make healing happen. If I find that while I'm standing in silence to direct my attention to make something happen to direct some kind of force to heal I'm on the wrong road. Such attitude actually interferes with the lines of communication. It serves as a block in the lines of the intercessory communication process. For the act of intercession is asking someone else who able to do the work. That someone is the Divine. So I get busy doing something. I clean, do dishes, work on the computer, go for a walk, all the while keeping my attention on the back burner so to speak, on alert that God is doing something. Whatever that is, I accept, not trying to direct. God knows better what is needed than either of us as Giver or as a Receiver.

## Physical Sensations

While working long distance you may experience physical sensations as tingling and warmth just as you do while working the hand positions with someone in person. You may experience the sensations in your hands or differently in parts or all over your body.

## The Giver

During these times as the Giver, I feel a sense of power activated moving through my body that something is going on. I can even tell the exact moment when the Receiver has laid down to accept the power of life and the moment he or she stops, simply by the ebb or flow of the sensations of power. Noticing the sense of power can be a distraction and with that awareness the temptation is to try to take on more responsibility than is yours to take and again attempt to direct the healing process. The sensations of power are also no indicator whether power is flowing or not. In the beginning of trying long distance it can be a helpful indicator for you the initiator or giver. . . sort of like "a sign." Remind yourself that you are not the source of healing and just let it flow. Stay neutral as possible. In other words, don't get in the way. It's the energy of the power of life flowing through you along the lines of communication. The source is from elsewhere, not directly from you.

## The Receiver

For the Receiver, the person may also feels tingling and warmth in parts or all over the body just as when you may be working together in person. In fact, be prepared that the sensations may even be more pronounced. Sometimes the person may even feel a heat sensation through out the whole body, and depending on the person may even break out in sweats. There can be difference with this kind of heat as well than with a topical or surface heat a person may experience while working the hand positions in person. This heat may well be experienced as coming up from deepwithin them, at the very core of their being. I have found that just as every person unique there can be unique responses. If a Receiver's response is to get up and jump around in glee instead of feeling heat then. . .why not?!

## What To Expect

At the end of this process, the Receiver may not be able to explain what the session was like. It can be such a profound experience of something so different than they ever experienced before that there often won't be words to describe what may have happened. Often I hear. . .

- "It was just different. . . I'm different"
- "I can't explain it."

There can be very subtle changes in the person's life with long distance intercession. This kind of therapy works on the whole of the person not generally just a body part when taking the route of the no hands approach.

## Story

I worked with a lady in another state who was had an unusual and severe viral infection where the doctors had no explanation of the nature of the cause or how to treat it other than with antibiotics. The problem was going on for months showing no signs of decreasing the severity of the infection. It was a health problem that to date had no name yet given to it being so unknown. Everyone involved was baffled.

So we tried long distance intercession together. With each session she would experience intense internal heat rising up "from somewhere within" that spread throughout the whole of her body. For the first two sessions there was no real noticeable physical change but other aspects of her life were being effected.

"I don't know what the change is, I'm just different somehow," was her response to the feeling. Something was changing within the nonphysical areas of her emotional, mental and spiritual life which revealed themselves as the weeks went by in family, work, purpose and even living conditions.

After the third session together all signs of the infection then disappeared. It could be the antibiotics finally helped being the only factor that made for the healing while the long distance work could have worked only with other aspects of her life, or with both. I don't know. All that we do know is that she no longer has the illness and her life is moving forward at a new pace of changes in growth.

I don't predict what will happen for someone during long distance intercession. It's different for everyone for everyone's needs are different. As a Giver during the process I can never properly judge the needs of the individual. That's why I take the position of remaining a neutral observer and let the true Giver of the power of life do the job.

## A Story

Here's an example of what I mean by not being able to predict what can happen during a session.

Once I was working with a woman who had a blood disease disorder that she was requesting help with. She was also wanting to schedule a massage appointment with me to help work out some severe physical aches and pains she was having that developed through an accident. We first scheduled a time to meet for long distance for the blood complication.

The next day I ran into Glenda after a meeting we were both attending and she told me what happened during the long distance session the night before.

"How did the long distance session go for you," I inquired.

"Actually, I forgot all about it to start with. The kids were running around the house yelling and screaming. For a while there it was chaos. One wanted to sit in my lap. I was holding her when suddenly my whole spine got hot from the back of my head down to the base of my hips. I looked up at the clock and it was nine o'clock, the time we had scheduled the long distance session together. The heat continued for thirty minutes until nine thirty when our session was supposed to end. Then the heat just quit."

"Well then how do you feel today?," I asked. I was curious.

"Wonderful!" she said. I don't have an ache or pain in my body.

We didn't schedule the massage. Not great for business but great for her!

So, you see, you may start out with one kind of intention and something else happens that is not at all what either you, the Giver or the Receiver may expect. With Glenda's case the healing process worked to heal her of what appeared to be more of an immediate problem than what she had asked about for that session. Neither one of us could have predicted that outcome.

## One More Story

I received a call from a relative in California who I had mentioned on a recent visit to call me if she ever got sick. We could try out long distance and see how it would help her. Her call was a request for a friend of hers who was sick. That was fine by me! She didn't inform me what the problem was and I didn't ask, for I've found too that it isn't particularly necessary to know what the problem is. So we set to work for a thirty minute session.

During the session I had the impression he had a sinus and an ear infection problem, receiving images of the sinus area and the left inner ear. (A little on the right ear) Also some kind of need throughout the body in his skeletal system.

I called back after the session, curious to know what happened to the friend.

They we're together through out the session so he was there to answer the phone.

"Hi Steve, how did the session go?" I asked.

"This is really different." he said calmly.

"It felt like I had a complete chiropractic adjustment. I felt a mild pressure on both sides of my head. It didn't hurt. It just felt like my head was being gently held by some kind of pressure while every bone in my body adjusted."

"Wow!" I said, being surprised myself. I still didn't know what the particular health problem was about. Then he informed me.

"I've been having a sinus problem for days now. Constant running but it all dried up and the dripping has stopped. Thank God!"

Venturing out to test my impression of his ears, I asked,

"Have you been having ear troubles too? I got the sense of your left ear and a little on the right have been giving you problems."

"Yes, I'm always having troubles with ear infections but it seems OK now."

"Well, good for you!" I respond.

We chat a bit further about the session before hanging up.

In this case I didn't have a clue what the health problem was. Not only did his sinus and ear problems clear up but he got a body adjustment to boot! That was completely unexpected. I can only guess the body adjustment may have been helpful in clearing up the health problem being partially involved in the reason for the sinus problem originally being called for. So you never know! I can only say go with what happens, which can often bring experiences that seem to have little to do at first with what you, the Giver and Receiver expect is needed to assist in the healing process.

## Time Limits

The work of healing is an art. It always has been and more than likely will always be. It's about learning what works and doesn't work. So don't stop at just one session after a single effort of attempting to be an intercessor for healing. Keep at it. Start with beginning to stick with the work for the duration of the time you and the Receiver have pre-determined. Your time agreements can vary as desired due to time constraints, or ability of either party to stay put. Go with what you are able. Try an hour or maybe ten minutes.

If the Receiver finds a reason to stop short of the agreed time that's up to them and their own sense of timing and awareness of the beginning or ending of the process of healing for the moment. After a time, a sensitivity of mutual communication maybe develop. In my experience there comes a knowing that is communicated between all parties that what has been done is enough, and the process ends for that time.

For people with serious health problems where I work with them in long distance intercession I suggest we do:

- Once or twice a week sessions together, for a
- Minimum of three to six weeks, and
- Evaluate the progress as we go along.

You can do the same. Try it. You have nothing to lose. It's an adventure to take part of such a learning process as the art of healing, and about the great mysteries involved waiting to be discovered as you go along.

# Wave Therapy

## Questions and Answers

# Questions and Answers

## Common Questions

### *Q. Can anyone work Wave Therapy and get results, or can only special people with "the gift" work Wave Therapy for healing?*

Wave Therapy is not about being gifted. It's about working in co-operation with the natural laws of creation that everyone has in common with their bodies. The only time where it appears to be a gift is when one person has a better flow of energy working flowing than someone else. That flow can be increased by anyone who is willing to practice the work. Wave Therapy begins with science; the provable and tested result of laboratory effects of the energy that flows in and out of the hands of human beings. Even animals have this energy. All physical things in existence are held together through magnetism. No one is exempt. So everybody has it. Knowing that it is there and practicing proven techniques such as are outlined in this book can provide you with the tools to experience effective assistance to others in their ability to heal naturally.

### *Q. I don't feel any tingling sensations or warmth in my hands. Does this mean I have no magnetic influence to help someone?*

What it means when you don't feel the magnetic sensations of tingling or warmth in your hands is that you don't feel it. The positive and magnetic influences are flowing through you. You're just not sensitive to it yet. Keep at it and you will eventually feel it. Regardless of whether you feel it or not the power of life flowing along the magnetic lines of force is at work. In my first experience that resulted in helping another person's knee to heal I didn't feel anything at all.

Often when I attempt to demonstrate to people that they have magnetic influence of the power of life flowing through their hands, (where I have them hold up their right hand facing my left that connects our magnetic field) I don't feel anything when they do. So the power is there. Feeling or not feeling energy makes no difference with whether the law of magnetism is working. It doesn't change according to how we feel about it, or in feeling it.

So if you don't feel anything at first keep at it. The benefits will happen for the person you're working on just the same.

### ***Q. Does it take a strong sense of faith to make the therapy work?***

Wave Therapy works regardless of strength or weakness of the traditional kind of faith. That's because the principles of Wave Therapy work on laws. The faith comes in your actually believing enough in the laws of  nature where you to try it out and see for yourself that action gets results. Once you get a result, you will notice a sense of confidence grow. That builds positive faith. When we put our trust in something that doesn't work we often think it's because we don't have enough faith. Putting your trust in the laws of magnetism that the Creator put into existence to move the power of life through us is placing your trust in something that works for positive results. Now that's faith!

### ***Q. Can I get sick by taking on other people's bad energy?***

I haven't noticed much of this yet in my own practice. I've worked on hundreds of people from broken toes, (never taken on the energy of the broken toe before) to headaches to AIDS.  With viral health problems, I do take common sense precautions and wash my hands after a session. I even get some fresh air.

The idea that people can take on another person's energy as though magnetizing their disease to their own magnetic field is a proper concern. I know people this happens with. However, I believe that the attitude of the practitioner is the key element that prevents taken on another person's health problems. Energy follows thought. What I believe and think has impact on the way energy works within and around me.

My attitude is that I'm helping another person to gain strength to overcome whatever it is they come to see me for help with. That same strength flows through me. My attitude is I don't allow the disease to effect me. It's as though I let it flow on by.

Often I combine my thoughts with physical action of breathing. I breathe in fresh new air that has energetic power in it and breath out the old. I believe energy follows what my thoughts move it to do. Apparently it works, I've never gotten ill from working with someone. Sometimes though I feel like I'm surrounded by an influence of bad energetic influence. I don't ignore that. When it happens I take time out to stand still and do a simple Body Sweep on myself. (Holding palms facing me on each side and sweep down.) Sometimes I "clear" myself by holding my left palm facing upward at my side with my right palm facing downward, like the Putting In position only arms are outstretched to my side. I hold for a few minutes allowing fresh new energy to flow through me cleaning me out, washing away any "bad" energy that may have come through to me from the other person.

Before each whole body session where more intense work is involved not only with the energy field of the body but also of the mind of the spirit and the soul, I offer a prayer. I model the prayer after the Lords Prayer adapting for each individual situation. I close the prayer with a request for protection against any negative influences and to be surrounded by the protective presence of the light of God. I also request any angels to be sent He would deem best to assist.

Another precaution I take is to clear the room after a session. I spray the air with something fresh and cleansing. I like to use incense too. I use sandalwood. I never used incense before until I started this work. It's effective in lightening up the room. So I use it. I also have an air cleaner, because I do a lot of work with people. I also offer a prayer of protection.

All in all, I'd say take common sense approaches to proper cleansing of yourself like you would in any circumstance being around people with viral problems.

### Q. Do you have to believe in God to do this therapy?

No.

But, I do.

I believe the therapy is working with God. I hold that all power comes from God[15] to maintain balance and harmony in the physical universe governed through the natural laws of magnetism. The great thing about accessing this energy is that its a freebie. No strings

[15] Psalm 62:11

attached. Whatever your belief it makes no difference in the workings of a law. It's works regardless of what a person believes.

I do believe that practicing Wave Therapy will challenge a person over time who may carry a belief that God doesn't exist. Whatever a person's idea, perception or belief of who God is or name attached to the concept of God, Wave Therapy is plain and simple contact with power that is greater than any of us. That alone over time should give anyone cause to ponder. We can't change the Law. We can't do a thing about altering the power that is there, only participate in it. The physics law of magnestim is a magnificent wonder of nature that demonstrates the perfect order and harmony of the universe. To me that's shows a well laid out plan beyond mere coincidence. Whatever a person's beliefs may be about who or what God is, the power is there. Let's work with it and reap the benefits it has for us on our health and wholeness.

***Q. If people are left handed is the magnetic field reversed in their body? If so, will I have to work Wave Therapy backwards?***

It's a popular notion that left handed people have reversed polarity. It's a myth. I'm sure that can be a relief if you may have considered Wave Therapy would have to be somehow worked backwards for those with reversed polarity. That would be an ordeal! Now you know you don't have to avoid left handed folk who want to enjoy the benefits of Wave Therapy work.

There are cases where people have reversed polarity but it has nothing do with being left handed. Just as being right handed has nothing to do with the cause of how the energy flows in our bodies. The energy flows because it does what it does. Generally speaking energy flows from right to left; always has most likely always will. Just like a car battery. The electricity in a car battery flows from the right positive (+) terminal to the left negative (-) terminal. Nothing can change that because that's how electricity in batteries work. (Unless fiddled with.) It's the same in the body. Though with some people, a very rare percentage seems to be the exception. How that happens isn't all that simple to figure out. Many things may cause it. It could be where a person lives has a big influence. I've read in farmer's agricultural books that underwater streams beneath houses can cause reversed polarity. Power lines, accidents, and attitudes can also contribute to reversed polarity problems. Whatever the cause, the working of Wave Therapy doesn't change overall. The only hand position that makes a difference is in your working around the head with a Closed Loop. For a person with reversed polarity, the left side will be positive and the right side will be negative. You would do a Closed Loop from the front of the person if it's a case when not working a whole body session to help balance and correct polarity With most people you will work from the back holding the Closed Loop position.

The other place you may notice a complaint from the person who has reversed polarity is at the feet. When holding a regular position of the left hand to right foot and right hand to left foot, they won't like it. You can choose to turn around and hold the position with your hands behind you palms facing their feet. This will match their polarity and ease discomfort. However, in the long run the person's polarity will still be reversed. Otherwise see it through when working a full body session to help correct the polarity.

Here's what I do:

- Hold the normal grounding foot position.

The person will go through some discomfort feelings. Remain in the position for up to ten minutes.

If this position gets uncomfortable to where the Receiver gets to uneasy you can speed the process along a lot more comfortably.

To assist in more rapid change try:

- Your left hand at the left ankle and hold the right hand above the left knee. Next stop. . .
- Move the left hand upward to just below the left knee and move the right hand above the left hip.
- Then place the left hand just below the left hip and the right hand above the left shoulder. You're creeping along the body in sections to direct the flow of energy.
- At the head hold the regular Closed Loop position.
- Then begin working down the right side of the body in the same way you worked up the left.

- Once back at the feet hold the standard grounding position.

This will help correct the polarity of the body.

### Q. What about children? Are they able to work Wave Therapy?

Absolutely! Kids are people, too. In fact you'll find if you ever have a child to work with you you'll notice strong magnetic influence of the power of life there. Kids are great and powerful workers of Wave Therapy. They have wonderful flow. Maybe, it's because they're growing still and require more intense energy flows to make this happen. It could also be that they just don't have adult concerns over what is possible and not possible. They're adventurous, curious, eager, and ready to step right up in using their imaginations. Energy follows thought. Thoughts of kids often live in the world of the impossible being possible.

I've worked with children who visibly see the magnetic field easily. (Or aura) Their sense of the spiritual is open to discovery. One child was in the room while I was working with his mother and he calmly asks, "Who is that standing over there in the corner?"

When I looked there was no one there, but he saw someone. It more than likely was an angel coming to minister. That happens a lot in my practice.

Kids are sensitive and strong in energy flow. So I would encourage any child in a home to participate in Wave Therapy. Besides it's a great way to get family involvement. Imagine, instead of sitting around watching TV you and the kids could be assisting each other in healing. Now that would be an evening.

### Q. What about the 10 minute rule? Is it a must to keep to that or can I go longer? Are there any circumstances that call for holding a position longer in one spot?

The ten minute rule is there to keep potential healing crisis at a minimum. Wave Therapy is an assistance to others in building up energy in the body where it's being depleted from having to work at keeping up health. Say, you break a bone. Energy is going to be needed for the body to heal. So the body sends energy to the area, drawing off resources from other areas of the body. If the body is low on energy and doesn't have enough or minimum amount of energy to do the job of healing, then energy drawn to heal depletes reserves for the rest of the body. If you're low on energy it may take longer to mend the bones back together.

Adding energy to the area such as using the Drawing In position helps increase the flow of negative energy to the area. Then the body doesn't have to draw off other areas to do the work. Now, too much energy can speed up the healing rather quickly and cause discomfort in the area. That's a healing crisis. So the ten minute rules helps to keep sufficient amount of energy but not too much or more than the body needs at one time.

There are times when it is advisable to pass beyond the ten minute rule. When someone's health is very serious and demands critical attention I've found you do whatever it takes. Here's a story of just such a circumstance.

## *Story*

I was on a trip with my parents traveling to Israel. When entering the hotel for our stay in Jerusalem my Dad swooned against the wall when we reached the staircase to the reception desk in the lobby. He had been sick and we had no idea. Dad doesn't take much to complaining about how he feels.

He was so sick that he was delirious with high fever and had no idea even where he was at.

The doctor was called and from what he could determine Dad had pneumonia. The doctor was limited in medications on hand and could only supply us with over the counter pain tablets. We were told to get him to bed, wait for a couple of hours, and if he doesn't get any better then to call and they would send an ambulance to take him to the hospital. (I don't know why if there was a concern that he was that bad they didn't take him immediately, but they didn't. We obeyed the instructions in our fright and took him to bed.)

I instructed Mom in holding the Drawing In position at his back. (He slept on his side) She did.

She held that position for her husband for one hour. Within that time the fever left him, he calmed down and fell asleep. She continued holding the position for another hour. Seeing he was at least improved I went to bed.

When I awoke in the morning both my curiosity and concern got me to their room immediately to see how he was. He wasn't in his bed! He was in the bathroom. I asked Mom how he was (Apparently better for he now knew where he was enough to find the potty) and Dad came out of the bathroom. He was perfectly fine. Acted as though not a thing had happened and he was getting ready for breakfast.

The whole dining hall turned and looked at us when we came in to the room, for they all could not believe their eyes. They had seen how sick he was the night before. We had a lot of curious guests at our table for that breakfast.

So there are times in critical health complications where extended time is more than helpful if not necessary. The only thing I can tell you is to go by the feel. Even wait in such cases till the tingling sensation goes away. When it does you'll know then the body has had enough. Then you have your direction to stop.

Otherwise, keep to the ten minute rule.

### *Q. When do I know it's best to use the Closed Loop or Drawing In?*

When there is pain it's always better to first try out using Drawing In. Drawing In uses the influences of negative magnetic energy which by nature always calms, soothes and diminishes pain. Any pain will decrease in time using the Drawing In position.

The Closed Loop will also help in diminishing pain because it does offer the negative polarity effects of negative magnetic energy from the left hand. It also uses the power of building up and strengthening the comes from the influence of positive magnetic energy of the right hand.

Pain due to arthritis is an example of when the Closed Loop seems to work well without the complication of strengthening pain. It builds up the strength of the hand, breaks down calcium deposits in the joints and diminishes the pain all at the same time.

The best way to know in any given situation is to ask the person you're working on how it feels. Is the pain increasing or decreasing? Questions can be the best thermometer to measure how things are going. If the pain is increasing while using the Closed Loop, then switch to Drawing In. Although overall recovery may happen with the Closed Loop more quickly, the price to pay sometimes is in increased temporary pain. Do the person a favor and do more Drawing In work, rather than put them through a healing crisis.

Here's an example.

When working on an ear infection with someone I once used the Closed Loop, instead of using solely the negative energy of Drawing In. The Closed Loop is powerful combining both positive and negative energies. The work was effective for within the hour the person was free of any ear pain. To reach that condition meant going through a temporary increase of pain far more than what she came into the session with. The lighter calming effects of the Drawing In position would have been just right. The added positive influence of the Closed Loop which gives strength, also can strengthen pain, causing a healing crisis. The increased effects of pain could have been avoided altogether by only using Drawing In.

### *Q. Is there any time I can injure someone with Wave Therapy?*

Outside the effects of the healing crises that is an over reaction to speeded healing in one area over another, the only time you can cause a possible injury is with the head and heart. All though I've never encountered any problems because I follow these guidelines.

- I keep to the 10 minute rule and
- I keep to the Closed Loop from behind the head. (The exception is when someone's polarity is reversed)

The other rule is with the heart. I only do the Closed Loop while standing at the receiver's LEFT side. Why? The front side of the body is negative in polarity and the back side of the body is positive in polarity. With this position I match the polarity of the body with my hands. For the left hand is also negative for the front of the body and right hand is positive for the back side.

I generally use Putting In or positive energy on the front side of the body when working with the heart. Primarily because of the thymus gland is located there which regulates the T-Cells that are the primary cells that regulate the body's immune system. That should always be increased not decreased. Positive magnetic influence of the right hand always increases and the negative of the left hand decreases. So I use Putting In.

If you keep to the rules you will never have any situations where you can potentially harm someone.

### *Q. Should a person remove any jewelry, leather, or silk garments while working Wave Therapy?*

I used to ask people to remove all clothing that I believed would get in the way of the flow of energy. I don't ask them to do that anymore, for I haven't really noticed any difference to bother with whether they wear the stuff or not.

To simplify my reasons there are basically three kinds of energy: magnetic, electrical, and spiritual.

Magnetic energy flows through everything. It's in, around, and moves through all that exists. Nothing stops it. Electrical energy however can be stopped by glass. We need electrical energy in our bodies. Power lines, some metals, insulation as with leather, can effect the balance and flow of electromagnetic energy. That's why it is sometimes suggested to remove clothing like silk, leather shoes and belts, watches, and some types of metal jewelry. To know what to do, I would say, go with your own experience and gut.

Spiritual energy is another story. What affects the flow of this kind of energy is our wills. Attitudes and beliefs that reflect our wills like, "Do I want to be healed or not to be healed." can make a difference in the flow of spiritual energy in our lives that deals with wholeness in body, soul and spirit. This kind of energy is both magnetic and electrical, yet in essence far more being made up of light, an attribute of the Divine Creator. Any type of clothing makes no difference for this energy to do its work for it is the power of life itself. If a person is determined that Wave Therapy won't work for them the resistance to the flow of energy may have the cause in a resistance to be well. This isn't putting out an excuse for lack of effectiveness of Wave Therapy principles rather it demonstrates even more the power our wills have in managing health.

One more question for now. Then for some closing comments.

***Q. What about medications? Do I stop taking prescribed medications in order for Wave Therapy to be effective?***

Never substitute Wave Therapy for following directions in taking medications or any advice prescribed by your health care practitioner. Wave Therapy is not meant to be a substitute for competent health care but instead be complimentary health management. I do suggest that anyone be watchful of the effects Wave Therapy can have in amplifying the strength of medications. It would be a good idea to inform the health care practitioner involved of participation in Wave Therapy especially if continued whole body work-ups are scheduled. I've noticed that the balancing effects and increased energy experienced through Wave Therapy can allow for medications to work more effectively. For instance, I had a man once who came to see me for a whole body work-up. The medications for pain were not working for him with his particular health complication. After the session those pills kicked right in! A health care provider should know the reasons behind why at one time a medication hadn't been effective and for some unknown reason it suddenly is. By letting him or her know what you're doing a more informed decision about your health care can be provided.

I also recommend that anyone practicing full body work-up sessions with focus on psychological and/or spiritual concerns have their therapist, social worker, counselor or spiritual director be informed as well to help with any healing crisis that may develop that may result in released emotions or memories. Anyone who works with Wave Therapy who is not trained in these areas should not attempt to offer advice or counseling. Leave this area to the professionals.

# FINAL THOUGHTS

More and more people are beginning to take responsibility for their own health, taking it upon themselves to discover new ways, to understand and apply effective self-health care in their efforts of becoming more whole. There is much to learn. Wave Therapy is one tool to take another step in taking part in that life-long healing journey of becoming whole.

This book is a presentation of my ongoing learning experiences in investigating the field of natural healing. It's a journey of discovering what works in assisting others to help managing their health by experimenting with approaches to the art of healing from many different resources. You can use the methods outlined here to help yourself and others in participating with your health. Practice and dare to experiment. You may find new and or better ways to add on to what I've presented here. If you do, by all means go for it! Change what works better for you or for others.

You may find ways yourself that differ with the methods outlined in this book. That's wonderful. That's the way of art. For instance, you may find you like to use your hands to touch a person rather than hold them at distance. The hands are tools. I choose the non-touch approach in order to feel the energy movement. That assists me in knowing energy is moving and something is happening. If you feel the energy moving while laying your hands on someone than go right ahead. What works, works. You may even find that you have a particular flair with assisting someone with one particular health problem than with another.

You will most likely find that not all healing comes quickly as you may like in many instances. There can be many different reasons why someone has a health complication. There could be deficiencies from diet reasons, lack of exercise, or poor attitudes that cannot and are not suppose to be permanently corrected by outside manual assistance. That job is up to the will of the person to take responsibility to be educated and act on proper health choices. There can be any manner of mixture of psychological and spiritual reasons as well behind any sickness. Investigate those areas. Human life and the task toward wholeness is not always as simple as following steps of one-two-three, you're well.

Pay attention. Listen. Listen to what the mind of your body, your soul and spirit tell you. Be willing to look within, learn and unlearn what you believe can be achieved in managing your health and taking up the challenge of the art of living well. Where there is pain, sickness, or disease due to blocks and leaks within the balance and harmony of life involving the relationships within the body, soul, and spirit, there is always a great Mystery out there and within willing and ready to help along the way.

Referring to the seven Power Centers for assistance can be a helpful tool in further discernment by taking a look at the whole of the person in regards to health involving the body, soul and spirit.

You will find with Wave Therapy that many health problems can be effected for the better with consistent practice of the therapy. Don't give up on the first try if the results you're looking for don't happen immediately or dramatically as you would like. Keep at it. Even Jesus had to take several shots at times in assisting another to heal. Remember the case of the blind man where he had to touch him twice to get full results for healing?[3] So, practice, practice, practice! The power of life will flow more readily and easily as you continue your efforts.

Where there is progress inform your physician what's going on to involve him or her. Your physician needs to be aware of everything your doing in your health management to make informed decisions about your care.

Wave Therapy can be a effective tool in your efforts in finding additional choices toward managing health and wholeness. It's a method of combining old fashioned methods of healing alongside conventional medicine. Practicing Wave Therapy will at the very least put you on the front lines of change as modern medicine marches on into the future where I believe we will more and more take up this ancient art now already becoming a part of tomorrow's new wave of energy medicine.

Hopefully, Wave Therapy has helped partly in the effort of opening up a new awareness about yourself and this great creation we are all a part of. The further task to recovery and wholeness can begin in taking advantage of the power that is already available to you that

---

[3] Mark 8:21-25, KJV

flows between your own hands. A free gift given to all that offers you and everyone the power to heal; the gift of the power of life!

Yours in healing,
Sam Winters

I would welcome hearing from you and your experiences with practicing Wave Therapy. To contact me concerning any questions or comments, for information on additional writings, audio and video tapes, or for workshops, please write to:

Sam Winters
The Center for Natural Healing Arts and Sciences
P.O. Box 1539
Wichita, Ks. 67201-1539

My e-mail address is:
samw@feist.com

# GLOSSARY

***Balance:*** A condition of harmony in body, mind and spirit where equal opposing forces are in equilibrium with one another.

***Block:*** Any force that interrupts or obstructs the proper balance and flow of energy to maintain health, whether that force be physical, mental or spiritual in nature.

***Body Sweep:*** A hand movement in Wave Therapy that seeks to pick up contaminated or toxic energy within a person's energy field that serves as a block or leak to the balance and harmony of health.

***Closed Loop:*** A hand position in Wave Therapy that engages both the positive and negative magnetic flow of the power of life.

***Drawing In:*** A hand position in Wave Therapy that engages solely the negative magnetic influence of the power of life to enhance the supply of negative energy to counter excess positive energy.

***Electromagnetic Field:*** The expandable field of force containing electrical charges in motion which are made up of both electrical and magnetic energy. These charges are negative, positive and neutral in nature. All healing of the body contains electromagnestism.

***Endocrine System:*** A system of ductless glands, such as thyroid or adrenal, of which the secretions of the cells of the glands move directly into the bloodstream.

***Energy:*** Power in action. A magnetic, electrical or spiritual force in motion.

***Energy Field:*** An oval or cocoon shaped matrix of electromagnetic energy that surrounds and penetrates all living and non-living things. All information concerning the make-up of the individual involving the physical, mental, and spiritual compartments of life are stored here. Sometimes called the aura.

***Equilibrium:*** Any condition in which all the power influences are equal resulting in a stable, balanced system.

***Harmony:*** To be in agreement. Where all individual ideas, thoughts, concepts, motivations, and actions of power work in combination as one working whole.

***Healing Crisis**:* A sudden change in opposing forces where deterioration or improvement in health is developing.

***Health**:* The state of being where all functioning is without disease or abnormality. Simply put, all is in harmony and balance between the physical, emotional and spiritual states of being. Health is a continual effort of balance between positive and negative energetic influences. A state of homeostasis.

***Homeostasis:*** A state of equilibrium produced by balance of functions in body, soul and spirit. To be in homeostasis is considered good health.

***Leak:*** Any condition of physical mental or spiritual health where energy leaves the individual.

***Lines of Force**:* A curved magnetic force associated with the meridians of magnetic influence surrounding an object corresponding to the magnetic force of the earth. Energy moves along these lines in circular motion.

***Magnet:*** A body that attracts or repels iron and other certain materials by the ability of the field of force within and around the object produced by the motion and the alignment of the atoms.

***Magnetism**:* The push/pull ability of a field of force produced by a magnetic/electrical current of positive, negative and neutral forces of polarity which binds the atoms of all physical matter together in creation.

***Metabolism:*** The physical and chemical process involved in extracting energy from sources containing the power of life.

***Negative Energy:*** One of two opposing forces in a magnetic field. An electrical force in nature that serves to calm, soothe, cause rest, and arrest of positive energy influence.

***Polarity:*** Alignment of opposing forces to work in harmony and balance.

***Polarity Balancing:*** A Wave Therapy move that acts to bring the opposing positive and negative forces of the poles of magnetism into balance.

***Positive Energy:*** One of two opposing force in a magnetic field. An electrical force in nature that serves to strengthen, build up and cause growth. Generally, all conditions opposing health are expressions of excess of positive energy.

***Power:*** The ability to act or perform effectively. A strength or force capable of being exerted to control, have authority to influence self or others.

***Power Centers***: Centers where energy moves in and out of the body involving the physical, psychological and spiritual use of power. There are seven major centers connecting the physical, mental, and spiritual energies in balancing the flow of the power of life. Also known as the chakras.

***Power of Life***: The force which animates and gives life. The source of which originates from the divine creator. This force flows as energy along the twelve major magnetic lines of force in the energy field.

***Putting In:*** A Wave Therapy position which enables increase of the flow of positive magnetic energy of the power of life.

***Reversed Polarity:*** Where the balance of opposing forces of negative and positive energy in a body flow in the opposite direction, from left to right rather than right to left.

***Scanning:*** A non-touch hand process of locating blocks and leaks of electromagnetic energy in the energy field.

***Wave Therapy:*** A spiritual science involving a non-touch hand method of manually influencing the natural flow of electromagnetic and spiritual energies of the power of life to assist others in the process of becoming more whole physically, emotionally, and spiritually.

# REFERENCES

and suggested reading

*Anatomy of the Spirit: The Seven Stages of Power & Healing,* Caroline Myss, Ph.D., Harmony Books, a division of Crown/Random House
*Biomagnetic Handbook: A Guide To Medical Magnetics The Energy Of Tomorrow*, William H. Philpott, M.D. and Sharon Taplin, Enviro-Tech Products
*Life Energy, Using The Meridians To Unlock The Hidden Power Of Your Emotions*, John, Diamond, M.D., Paragon House, New York
*Logos Bible Software Collection,* Logos Research Systems, Inc.
*Magnet Therapy: Balancing Your Body's Energy Flow For Self-Healing,* Hogen Hannemann, Sterling Publishing Co., Inc., New York.
*Magnetic Therapy,* Abott George Burke, Devorss & Company
*Mesmerism,* Doctor Mesmer, MacDonald & Co. (Publishers) Ltd., London, Great Britain
*Physics,* Cliffs Quick Review
*Power Of The Magnet To Heal,* Dr. A.K. Bhattacharya, Dr. Ralph U. Sierra, Dr. A.K. Bhattacharya
*The Healing Light,* Agnes Sanford, Phoenix Press,Walker and Company, New York
*The Orthodox Way,* Bishop Kallistos Ware, St. Vladimir's Seminary Press, Crestwood, N.Y.
*The Klutz Book of Magnetic Magic,* Paul Doherty, Ph.D., and John Cassidy, Klutz Press, Palo Alto, California
***The Relaxation Response***, Herbert Benson, William Morrow & Co., New York, NY
*The Magnetic Blueprint Of Life,* Albert Roy Davis and Walter C. Rawls, Jr., Acres USA
*The Body Electric:Electromagnetism And The Foundation Of Life, Robert* O. Becker, M.D., and Gary Selden, William Morrow and Company, Inc.
*The New Grolier Multimedia Encyclopedia*, The Software Toolworks Inc.

*The Self-Healing Workbook:Your Personal Plan for Stress Free Living,* C. Norman Shealy M.D., PhD, Element Books Limited
*The Magnetic Effect,* Albert Roy Davis and Walter C. Rawls, Jr., Acres USA
*The Orgone Accumulator Handbook; Construction, Plans, Experimental Use and Protection Against Toxic Energy,* James Demeo, Ph.D., Natural Energy Works, Al Cerrito, Ca.
*The Rainbow In Your Hands,* Albert Roy Davis and Walter C. Rawls, Jr., Acres USA
*Vital Magnetic Cure, An Exposition Of Vital Magnetism,* by a Magnetic Physician, Health Research
*Your Healing Hands; The Polarity Experience,* Richard Gordon, Unity Press, Santa Cruz

# Index

## A



## B



## C

## D



## E

## R



## S

## T



## U



## V



## W